Viking

Mars Expedition 1976

Library of Congress
Catalog Card Number:
78-55518

This dramatic photo on the cover was taken in early August 1976 as Viking II approached Mars. The Argyre Basin covered with frost is clearly visible at the bottom of the planet, while the gigantic Ascreaus Mons stands out at the top with clouds trailing into the wind. In the middle is the great rift canyon called Valles Marineris.

Opposite Page
On June 17, 1976, Viking I was 348,000 miles from Mars as this photograph was taken. The row of three volcanoes are the Tharsis Mountains while Olympus Mons, Mars' largest volcano, is toward the top of the picture.

Preface

This book has been prepared by Martin Marietta Aerospace, the principal industrial contractor to the National Aeronautics and Space Administration for its Project Viking lander, scientific experiments and mission integration. The material was assembled with the cooperation of Martin Marietta subcontractors, the Jet Propulsion Laboratory, NASA and the Viking science teams.

All photographs are the property of the National Aeronautics and Space Administration and have been made available with the cooperation of NASA and JPL.

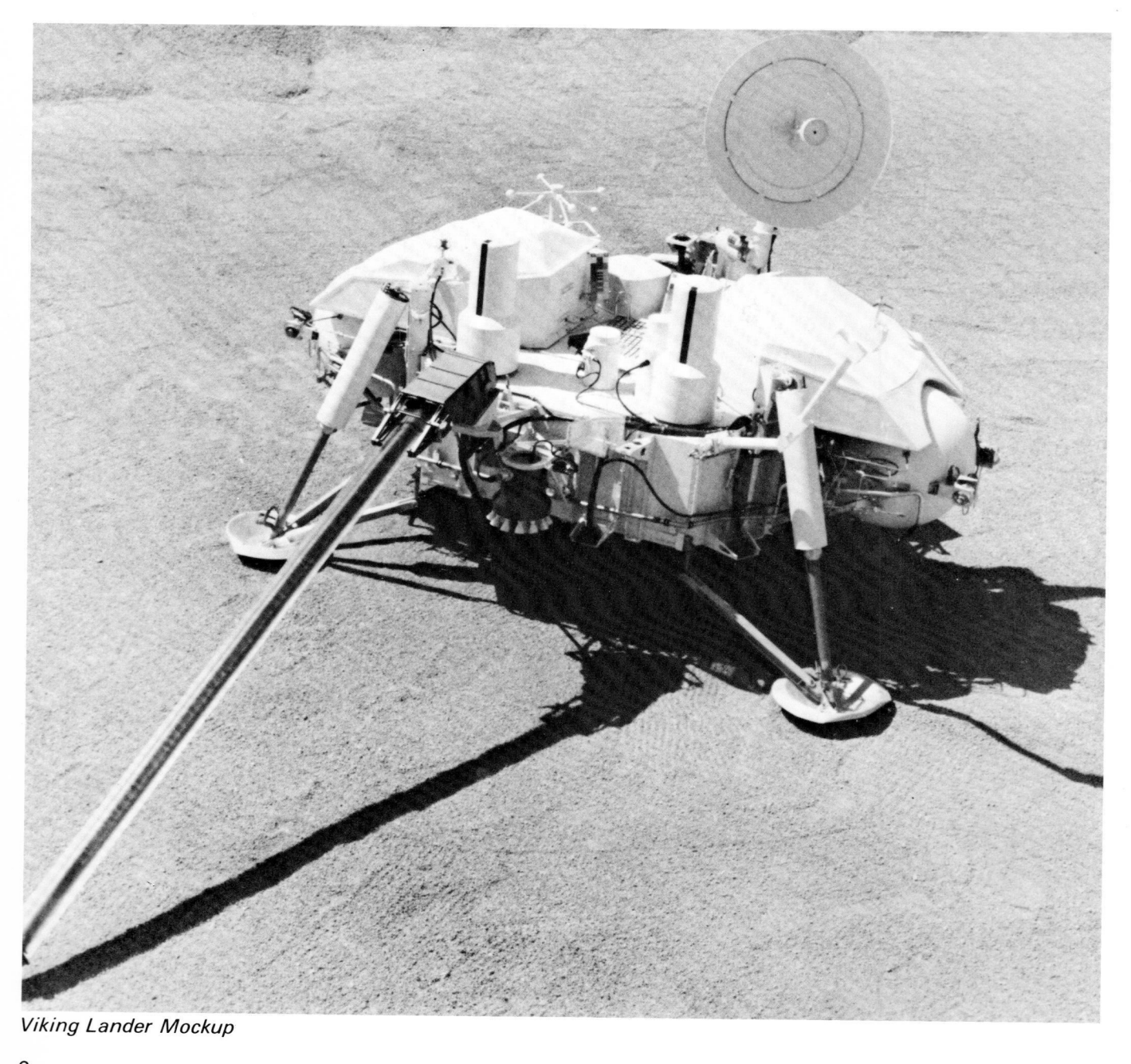

Viking Lander Mockup

Contents

JOURNEY TO MARS 9

UNDERSTANDING MARS
Pulling Back the Shroud of Time,
Dr. Gerald A. Soffen 15

The Biological Puzzle, Dr. Harold P. Klein 18

Search for Organics, Dr. Klaus Biemann 20

Martian Weather, Dr. Seymour L. Hess 22

The Frozen Planet, Dr. C. Barney Farmer..... 25

-225 F, Dr. Hugh H. Kieffer 27

100,000,000-Year-Old Floods,
Dr. Michael H. Carr 30

View from the Surface, Dr. Thomas Mutch ... 34

Measuring a Planet,
Dr. William H. Michael, Jr................... 37

Martian Atmosphere, Dr. Michael McElroy ... 39

On the Desert, Dr. Richard W. Shorthill...... 42

The Red Planet, Dr. Robert B. Hargraves 44

In Search of a Pebble, Dr. Benton C. Clark ... 45

Marsquakes, Dr. Don L. Anderson 48

LANDER PERFORMANCE 50

ORBITER PERFORMANCE 55

VIKING SCIENCE RESULTS SUMMARY 58

VIKING PROJECT MANAGEMENT 61

Journey to Mars

After more than 15 years of planning under the leadership of the National Aeronautics and Space Administration, the most sophisticated spacecraft built to date were launched in 1975 on a journey of more than 400 million miles toward the first landing on another planet of our solar system. This is the story of the fantastic success of the two historic flights of Viking spacecraft to Mars and a report of what mankind has learned from these journeys.

The first Viking spacecraft was rocketed toward Mars on August 20, 1975 and Viking II followed on September 9, 1975. Both launches came after minor delays. On Viking I, a faulty thrust vector control valve on the Titan III Centaur booster and a falloff in the normal charge of the spacecraft's batteries delayed the launch for nine days while the problems were corrected. Viking I left the launch pad at Cape Canaveral at 5:22 p.m. EDT, August 20. Viking II missed its scheduled launch date by eight days while a problem with the spacecraft's S-band radio subsystem was corrected. The launch took place on time at 2:39 p.m. EDT on September 9.

The interplanetary cruise phase of both Viking spacecraft lasted 310 days until Mars orbit insertion. Seven days into the first flight and 10 into the second, a midcourse maneuver, requiring the firing of the orbiter engine, put the spacecraft on a precision course for a rendezvous with Mars. On October 19, the Viking I lander batteries were given a full charge as part of their conditioning for future operations. On October 31 ground controllers discovered that the Viking II battery system could not be charged. By November 7, an alternative plan was used to charge batteries through a backup system, circumventing the inoperable prime charging system.

The next step was to make the spacecraft ready for high speed data relay. The Viking I orbiter high-gain antenna was put into operation November 12, with Viking II following suit on November 18. Both high-gain antennas were repositioned daily to keep the radio beams aimed directly at the Earth.

At the halfway point of its flight in mid-February 1976, Viking I was slightly more than 89 million miles from Earth and 15 million miles from Mars. Viking II was three million miles behind Viking I. Eighty-five days before reaching Mars orbit, Viking I was traveling at 61,000 miles per hour relative to the Earth and 5500 miles per hour relative to Mars and had flown 326.6 million miles. Viking II had flown 295.5 million miles and had reached a speed of 60,400 miles per hour.

By May 1, 1976 the Viking I cameras picked up the first faint pictures of Mars from 7,000,000 miles. The planet appeared as little more than a disc of light identified as the fringe of the south polar hood. To the human eye Mars would have appeared one-third the size of the moon as seen from Earth.

One hour before entering orbit insertion, the spacecraft was traveling 8000 miles per hour relative to Mars and was up to 9000 miles per hour at the time of orbit insertion. Orbiter rocket engine ignition took place at 3:38 p.m. PDT, June 19, 1976 and confirmation of engine shut down came 38 minutes later. The Viking then was positioned in orbit,

The Titan III Centaur booster lifts Viking I from the launch pad at Cape Canaveral, Fla. at 5:22 p.m. August 20, 1975.

requiring only a slight trim maneuver two days later to place the spacecraft in an orbit that passed over the preselected Viking landing site at its lowest altitude.

As more and more information was returned from the orbiter on the landing site, scientists became increasingly concerned with the site's selection. Using photographs, radar data, and other information, the scientists decided the primary site was much rougher than indicated by studies of Mariner IX photos and could, in fact, be covered with large boulders. On June 27, James S. Martin, NASA's Viking project manager, announced that the scientists would begin looking for other landing sites and declared the primary sites unsafe. The expanded survey delayed the first landing two and one-half weeks beyond the original projected landing date of July 4, the nation's 200th anniversary.

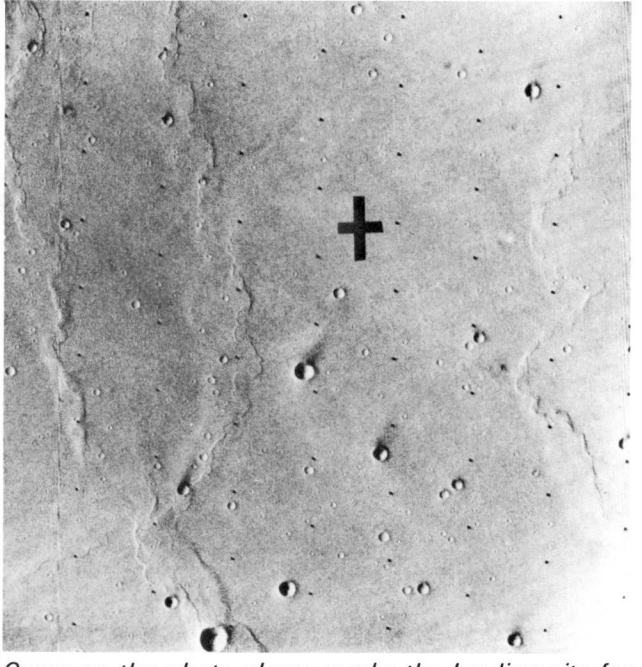

Cross on the photo above marks the landing site for lander I in the western portion of Chryse Planitia. At right, fault zones break the Martian crust with the fault valleys widened because of falling rock possibly caused by Marsquakes.

On July 1, following extensive study of the information, a new site was selected in the Plain of Chryse. Scientists decided it was a smoother area because sediment had washed down from the higher areas and settled, and there were less frequent craters. Signs of windblown features also showed up in the photos.

A trim maneuver July 8 placed the Viking I in a new orbit for additional surveillance of the site and eventual landing. Within a week the site had been certified and the landing scheduled for July 20.

Touchdown at 5:12 a.m. PDT on July 20 followed a perfect entry and landing sequence. The landing took place within 7 seconds of the predicted time, and the terminal velocity, predicted to be 8 feet per second, was actually 8.2 feet per second. The landing success was just the beginning — within minutes the camera operation and picture production astonished the flight team members as well as a national television audience. The reconstruction of the pictures on the control center monitors brought cheers of congratulations among the participants, some of whom had been involved in the program for 15 years.

Immediately after the Martian touchdown, the lander transmitted entry data to the orbiter to relay to Earth. The Viking lander then turned its S-band antenna for future direct communications with Earth. Next it ejected the surface sampler shroud, deployed the meteorology boom, activated the various scientific and engineering instruments, and began gathering data.

Meanwhile the orbiter continued to survey the landing area using its cameras, water vapor mapper and thermal mapper to give scientists a broader understanding of the environment and a better basis for interpreting the lander data.

Viking I landed in a stable position surrounded by light red or pink colored rocks that showed a mixture of processes at work on the planet, including crater impact debris, old volcanic material, wind stripping and water mixing. A panoramic picture showed the shock absorber at the top of a lander leg stroked approximately 3 inches, indicating that Viking landed on a solid surface.

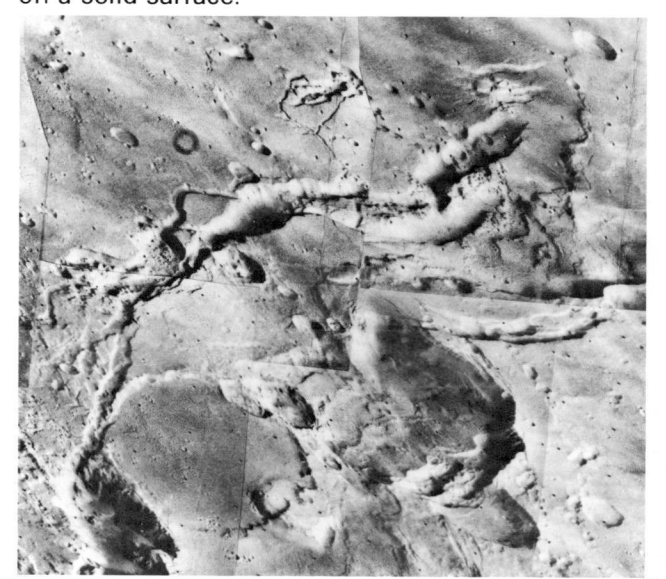

The first photograph was of the footpad. This gave scientists an opportunity to characterize the surface by examining the effect of the lander's impact. Pictures also showed the horizon to be about 1.8 miles away. A low ridge was visible, covered with rock debris darker red than the rocks seen in the foreground. It is thought to be the rampart of an old crater with the dark material being debris ejected by the impact. Lighter patches of sand closer to the lander appeared to be wind-filled craters. The Martian sky was brighter than expected and pink, with light scattering to a degree illuminating shadow detail much like some areas on Earth. Scientists estimated the Martian atmosphere may have particle counts and sizes similar to those in the Earth's atmosphere.

On July 23, ground controllers discovered that the soil sampler arm had not extended far enough to allow an inflight locking pin to drop free. Remaining attached to the boom, the pin became a stop-block preventing full retraction of the boom. The situation was quickly evaluated and simulated on the science test lander at JPL and the proof test lander at Martin Marietta Aerospace in Denver. New commands to the Viking I lander extended the boom to allow the pin to drop. Pictures verified the corrected condition of the collector head, located the fallen pin on the ground and the spacecraft assumed its normal operations.

Viking II joined the Viking I orbiter in Mars orbit at 5:30 a.m. PDT on August 7, 1976. The orbit realized by

Viking II was very close to the prescribed specifications. The spacecraft's elevation angle was such that it immediately took on the assignment of the morning photography of Mars while the Viking I orbiter took care of the afternoon camera work.

The flight team learned a lesson from the landing site problems of Viking I and changed Viking II's landing sequence. Rather than synchronizing the orbit with the landing site, Viking II was allowed to move around the planet surveying the entire latitude rather than a specific landing point. The area picked for the Viking II lander was in the Utopia Planitia. This is a large, broad plain located to the north and 4500 miles on the opposite side of the planet from the Viking I on the Plain of Chryse. The Utopia Plain is a low area, judged by scientists to have high concentrations of water vapor.

On August 25, 1976 an orbit trim maneuver stopped Viking II's westward walk around the planet. The engine fired for 23 seconds. This final trim secured the spacecraft's low orbital point over the landing site. The following days were spent certifying the chosen site and the readiness of the spacecraft for the landing sequence. When the sequence began, a problem developed that kept Viking scientists in suspense for hours to come.

Seven minutes after separation from the Viking II orbiter, contact with the lander was virtually lost. A

This is the first photograph from the surface of Mars, taken just minutes after the spacecraft landed July 20, 1976. Of immediate interest were rocks and the finely granulated sand or dust. The large rock in the center is approximately 4 inches across.

The top photo shows the first panorama from lander I photographed on July 23, 1976, revealing sand dunes and large rocks — the nearest being about 25 feet from the lander and about 10 feet in diameter later nicknamed "Big Joe." The horizon is about two miles away from the lander with thin clouds visible above it. Lander II photographed the bottom panorama shortly after touchdown September 3, 1976. The rocks strewn on the surface range in size up to several yards and those that are pitted resemble fragments of volcanic lava.

small amount of low-rate data was relayed back to Earth by the orbiter from the lander, indicating the lander was still operational. A power failure in the Viking II orbiter had caused loss of control of the orbiter and blacked out nearly all communications from the orbiter. In fact, for nearly 24 hours the only indication of a successful landing was the increase in the rate of information from the lander on the low-rate channel which is automatic with touchdown on the surface.

Seconds after the power failure, a backup system regained control of the orbiter and stabilized it. But during the few uncontrolled seconds, the change was enough to leave it without the necessary computer commands to tell the orbiter how to reorient itself. The orbiter's computer system shuts off automatically when such a problem occurs to keep the spacecraft from doing something it shouldn't. Once connected, the computers must be issued commands to reinstate their functions and to reorient the spacecraft to the high-gain antenna position. This did not occur in time for the first two pictures after landing to be transmitted on schedule. The bulk of the information was stored in the orbiter until it was able to

transmit the data to Earth. When received, the first photographs from Viking II were of very high quality. The Viking II lander actually settled down safely on the Utopia Planitia at 3:58 p.m. PDT on September 3, 1976.

Once both Viking landers were on Mars and operating, commands were sent to both orbiters to commence independent orbital walks around the planet to survey other surface areas. The orbiters were moved into subsynchronous orbits — one with an orbital period shorter than a Martian day. With the planet's rotation and orbital period out of synchronization, the orbiter no longer matches up with the same relative point on Mars. As a result it reaches its low orbital point at a different location on the same latitude each day. The spacecraft's orbital plane does not really move but from the surface it appears that the orbiter is moving east. It is a simple way to walk around the planet to survey, with the planet doing all the work.

The first survey of the planet by orbiter I took 13 days, beginning September 11 and ending September 24, 1976, during which time the Viking I lander reduced its activity, continuing only with biological experiments. After one revolution, orbiter I continued around until it was directly over the Viking II lander. It then became the relay station for lander II while orbiter II conducted some independent experiments. The success of the interchange meant that Viking orbiter II could move on its own to survey the northern area of Mars.

At the close of the highly successful primary mission, both landers continued to operate and support all science investigations with the exception of the lander I seismology experiment which failed to unlock after landing and remained inoperative.

The Viking extended mission, which began after conjunction, commenced November 29, 1976. During the extended mission — lasting more than 18 months — scientists continued to receive data from the meterorology, seismology, imaging and inorganic chemistry experiments.

Early in 1977 both Viking landers felt the Martian winter. Because of the extreme cold, lander II, which is 950 miles further north than lander I, was shut down. It still recorded and stored data, but suspended communications with Earth. Temperatures at the lander II site ranged during the day from about -180° F to 162° F and at the lander I site from about -135° F to -63° F. The temperature spread between day and

night at both sites also was much narrower than at the time of landing. The Martian winds at the lander sites changed direction and were much less variable than earlier in the season. Photos and weather readings were taken daily by lander I and scientists noted changes in the atmosphere with the changes in seasons.

Sampler head that gathers soil and rock samples for testing.

Thousands of rocks stretch to the horizon two miles away from lander II. The rock in the lower right corner is 10 inches across, the largest rock near the center of the photo is about two feet long and one foot high. A small channel winds from upper left to lower right.

The orbiters continued to operate taking high-resolution photographs and performing water vapor and thermal mapping. They also completed the photo mapping of the entire planet.

By extending the mission, NASA made use of the spacecraft to obtain seasonal variations, long-duration sampling for statistically important experiments and data not possible during the primary mission because of time constraints. The meteorology studies also benefited from the additional time as they needed significant statistical data for long term trend interpretation. The seasonal coverage, coupled with supporting data from instruments on the orbiters, will permit global atmospheric modeling with a resultant improved understanding of Martian weather.

The longer time span was useful to seismology experiments because of the random occurrence of events. Dust storms presented new opportunities to analyze the material deposited near the lander. These data will provide a perspective from which to anaylze material dug by the soil sampler from beneath the surface.

The first clear indication of frost accumulation on the Martian surface was recorded in this photo taken by lander II on September 13, 1977, late in the Martian winter. Whether the frost is water or carbon dioxide or a combination of the two is not known. Nighttime temperatures were -171°F., although at the time the photo was taken the temperature was -144°F.

Understanding Mars

Excerpts of interviews with members of the science teams who planned the Viking experiments are given in the following chapter.

Pulling Back the Shroud of Time

Science Steering Group: Gerald A. Soffen (Chairman), Viking Project Office, Langley Research Center; R.S. Young, (Vice Chairman), Viking Program Office, National Aeronautics and Space Administration; A. Thomas Young (Secretary), Viking Project Office, Langley Research Center; Conway Snyder, Jet Propulsion Laboratory; and the science team leaders.

Dr. Gerald A. Soffen

I think we've moved from thinking about Mars as a simple, stationary place, to thinking about it as something we can compare with our Earth. That's our plan. The one thing I think that will really last longest, once the years go by and we forget about whether we discovered nitrogen or whether we discovered this, that or the other thing, is the fact that during the Viking project we began to understand Mars as not just a single place, but a world that goes through changes and has a history, a history that's not as big a mystery as it has been. The shroud of time has been pulled back and we begin to see Mars, in a small way, as it may have been during its origin, as it may have been in the path of its history, and much more, of course, in its normal, annual, and even daily cycles. Maybe, with some luck, we will go through a full Martian annual cycle, which is nearly two years on Earth.

Interlocking, in my mind, are two major arenas of thought that underlie all that happens on Viking. One major line of thought deals with water and the atmosphere and the past history of Mars. The other major arena of thought lies in the chemistry of the surface, not only whether it's biological, chemical, or otherwise, but also that whole chemical arena of how the very thin top crustal layer of Mars got the way it is.

Certainly the discovery of nitrogen must rank among the very important accomplishments. Nitrogen, by itself, would be important, but the isotopic abundances of nitrogen and other gases, for example argon or the trace gases of krypton, xenon and neon, have really given us a feeling for where the atmosphere came from. But what happened to it? We still don't understand the history of Mars. But we do have some feeling for, given today's atmosphere, what it must have been like some time ago. In the relatively recent past, or the last few million years of Mars history, some fairly dramatic and major changes took place. It wasn't a single change. It wasn't a change that all of a sudden started happening. It was a change in the atmosphere, a loss in the atmosphere. The atmosphere was being affected by the Sun's radiation, being swept away and actually diminishing in size. What we are left with today is maybe only 10 percent of the original atmosphere on Mars. The loss of anything as substantial as 90 percent of an atmosphere must have affected the history of the planet.

The single thing that stands out in my mind is the impact that it would have on water. Water, as we all know, is the magic molecule as far as life is concerned. It is the essence of life. It is what life is all about. It is what the Earth is all about. While it is seemingly a simple molecule, water is not a simple

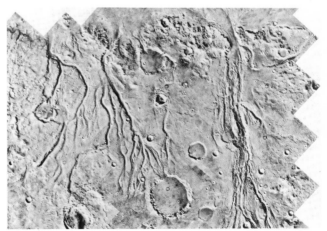

This mosaic is made up of pictures of the Mars surface taken from orbiter I on four separate revolutions. The channels are suggestive of a massive flood. The source of the floor is not known. In several cases, the channels cut through craters, where in others, the craters clearly occurred later than the floor and are superimposed in the channels.

molecule at all. Water can change in state from gases, to liquids, to solids. Before we went to Mars we knew there was some gaseous water. We know now there is a lot of gaseous water. Before Viking we had thoughts about there being permafrost, and now there certainly is powerful evidence of permafrost. And there is plenty of solid water at the poles of Mars. But now we really believe there has been a massive inundation, a tremendous catastrophic flooding of the surface. The only way you can account for all that water is with a significantly different atmosphere in the past. Mars is like the Earth in the sense that at one time it had an atmosphere large enough to allow flowing rivers and flowing water to carve up the surface and give us all those dramatic features. What we are seeing from the orbiter is the old Mars and the remnants of all that impact on Mars over the many tens, hundreds of millions of years — the terrific volcanism on Mars, the considerable fluvial activity.

On the lander scale, we're seeing sort of today's Mars or yesterday's, or maybe last year's at most. It's like seeing your own backyard on Earth. You're not really seeing the history of Earth, you're seeing the effects that have taken place in recent periods. You sometimes have to back off to get these large-scale perspective views of history. I think that really one of the major accomplishments of Viking is under-

On its 14th orbit on July 3, 1976, orbiter I took this striking series of pictures of Ganges Chasma showing several overlapping lobes of material (A.) which have slid into the canyon. Other notable features include a dune field at the lower right (B.), and layered material apparently volcanic in origin at the top of the far canyon wall (C.). Conical hills (D.) are of uncertain origin, but help make this a fascinating scene.

standing something about the major historical events that have taken place.

But let's look at the other problem area that perplexes and troubles me more. I feel we really haven't done justice to it. I'm not sure we can do justice to it. The thing that is so troubling to me is seeing a surface that chemically is very different from Earth. In the case of the moon, we came across material on the basaltic surface of the moon that, while it wasn't something you'd easily pick up — a clod full on Earth — was well known, well documented and we understood it. We even understood from the very beginning that the moon was basaltic. On Mars, in a sense, we have much more data than at a comparable point after the first lunar mission. We have an enormous amount of elemental abundance data, we have data that came out of the biology that was totally unexpected, and of course data that came from magnetic properties, from the picture images, and from the infrared sensors. You should be able to say "If I were there I would be able to pick this up and it would be like _____" — and there should be an answer for that blank. The trouble is there isn't an answer. There isn't anything on the Earth that really is quite Martian. I've talked to a number of scientists and they said that if you had some of the clay-like material from western Washington and laced it with some of the magnesium sulfate that's from the gypsum beds of the southwest, and then added this oxidizing agent or that superoxidizer or peroxides and then did this — that's a laboratory mixture, that's not a planetary mixture. What I'm troubled with is how did this planet, in a sense, get charged up? How did it get the way it is with as active a surface as it appears to have?

I think we really do not understand the full impact of the radiation on the surface, the desiccation of the surface, the way the elements have sifted out, the way the winds have behaved and certainly the absence of organic molecules. Many years ago when I first began on Viking, I didn't believe the biology was the most important thing we were doing. I always felt the biology might be ambiguous, whereas I thought the organic experiment would really give us an answer to a very major question. I had no doubt at all, just to show you how wrong I was, that there would be organics there. But could you distinguish between biologically generated organics and nonbiological organics? That simple question I felt would give NASA the impetus, the leverage, to tell us whether to go towards Mars in the direction of biology or in the direction of geology. We could finally get an answer to "Is the organic material on Mars of biological origin or was it not of biological origin?" I can well remember the day that Harold Urey, pounding on the table, said "Of course there are organics on Mars. It's only a question of where it came from." Now do we have an answer? At least at those two landing sites we have found no organic material. That comes as the biggest single surprise. It's made me think though "Do we really understand the origin of organic material here on Earth?"

I foresee the next year or two as being the high points for Viking. Many papers that were not generated by the project will be presented at scientific meetings. They'll be papers by some university student or professor who has been working on data and the wave of information Viking has produced. Hundreds of scientists throughout the world will be studying Viking data and making important discoveries beyond those made by the Viking scientists. Viking's data will be used in many ways to understand Mars, or even to reflect back on the Earth. I think about five years from now there will be papers still milking out the last bit of data.

I think that perspective is the word I would most associate with Viking in the sense it is what anyone expects with a pioneering exploration effort. Exploration is just that. You explore to get a perspective of where the things you ultimately study will fit into the overall.

The Biological Puzzle

The biology instrument conducted three experiments to search the Martian soil samples for living micro-organisms. All three involved the incubation of portions of the same sample under controlled conditions. The three experiments were the pyrolitic release experiment, which looked for the biological synthesis of organic molecules from labeled gases; the labeled release experiment, which looked for the assimilation of labeled nutrients with the release of gases; and the gas exchange experiment, which looked for metabolically caused changes in the composition of the gases in contact with living organisms.

The biology instrument was the single most complicated science instrument on the lander and performed a total of 21 analysis cycles on both landers. The scientific tests were conducted on a total of 18 teaspoons of surface material. The sample requirements per experiment were two teaspoons for the biology hopper, one-fifth of a teaspoon for the gas chromatograph mass spectrometer, and seven teaspoons for the X-ray hopper.

To acquire the soil with the best potential for life, the surface sampler unit moved rocks with the hopes of finding protected life underneath. Moving the rocks with a long thin shroud presented a problem as the rock would merely turn in place when pushed. After intense study, the scientists developed a new technique and a successful rock push took place.

Biology Team: Harold P. Klein (Team Leader), Ames Research Center; Norman Horowitz, Biology Division, California Institute of Technology; Joshua Lederberg, Department of Genetics, Stanford University School of Medicine; Gilbert V. Levin, President, Biospherics Inc.; Vance Oyama, Chief, Life Detection Systems Branch, Ames Research Center; and Alexander Rich, Professor of Biophysics, Massachusetts Institute of Technology.

Dr. Harold P. Klein

Before we landed on Mars we had a variety of opinions, ranging from those who expected to see no life on Mars to those who expected to see a rather flourishing — maybe not terribly advanced, but at least a flourishing life on Mars. I think we can say at this stage that, judging from the two landing sites and everything we have been able to gather on Viking including the imaging, biology experiments and chemistry experiments, those who expected to see very flourishing life on Mars were wrong. That means we must look more carefully at Mars and ask whether the sophisticated biology and the chemistry instruments have given us clues as to whether there might be some less obvious kind of life on Mars. Maybe life that is very sparse and may be so very small it is not obvious.

First, all of the data taken together seem to indicate that the two landing sites, although separated by some 4500 miles, have a surface material that, if not identical, is so similar we can't tell the two sites apart. If we make that assumption and then allow ourselves to go back and forth between the results from the two landers, we can develop some sort of scenario. I think we can say, first, that one pre-Viking model of Martian microbial life we were testing, namely the Oyama model, which says that Mars should have micro-organisms similar to large numbers of soil bacteria on this planet, did not pan out. At both sites, we have no indication to support that kind of a model or concept of Martian biology. That tells us either there are no organisms at all on Mars, which would not be a precise conclusion, or that no organisms fit that model.

In looking at the other two biology experiments, both give indications we could interpret on first inspection as being the result of some simple organisms being present. Here, however, we have to add the very important findings of the molecular analysis team, which found no detectable organic compounds in the samples of the Martian surface. These findings make us on the biology team very suspicious that the weak-to-moderate signals in the two biology experiments may not be due to biology because they should be accompanied by some organic material in the soil. However, the lack of organics, in and of itself, does not rule out the possibility of organisms but it makes that whole idea much less attractive. The sensitivity of the molecular analysis experiment allows us to say there are fewer than a million Earth-like bacteria per gram of Martian soil.

We also have evidence that the surface material of Mars contains chemicals that are highly oxidizing and could, in and of themselves, interfere with the biological tests and mimic them. Just as a living organism can, let us say, decompose a steak by eating it and digesting it, the steak can also be decomposed by being thrown into sulfuric acid, with roughly the same end products. The sulfuric acid in this case would be an inorganic, nonbiological oxidizing material. Since we're certain there are one or more of these inorganic materials on Mars, we then have serious doubts as to interpretation of the biological results. We tried a few tricks on Mars to see if we could devise some experiments that might definitely rule out the possibility that the decomposition seen is due to biology. We have not been able to do that so far. Everything we've tried, such as heat sterilization of Martian soil, affected the process as would be expected of living organisms and, therefore, has not ruled out the biological interpretation. Of course, this doesn't mean it's biology that we are seeing either. It just says that we haven't been able to rule it out.

Thus we are left with a reproducible set of results on Mars we've never seen with any terrestrial or lunar soils and that are quite unique in our experience. They fit a biological interpretation, but also must be regarded very suspiciously because we know that chemicals there could be obscuring or mimicking biological processes.

That leaves us with the pyrolytic release experiment and there we have some weak "positive" signals. However, based on the latest results from Mars, a biological interpretation for these weak positive signals appears to be untenable. Should ground-based tests now in progress hold up, then I think we will be able to say with a fair amount of conviction that what we have been seeing is not biology in this experiment.

Now that we are all finished on Mars, we are left first with one experiment, pyrolytic release, that at first seriously raised the possibility of biology but that we now believe is not likely to be true. The second experiment, the labeled release experiment, also showed us positive signals but we have not been able to unscramble these data so far on Mars. Finally, the third experiment, the gas exchange experiment, never did yield any positives in the sense of looking like biology.

But one other point must be made, not withstanding any of this. The data does not really say there is no life on Mars. We can certainly say that it is not rampant, but we can't be sure there isn't some scraggly form of life for which we just haven't found the right nutrients or the right location or the right incubation temperature or the right environment within which to show its presence. That's why it's going to be very difficult for me, at least, to come out and say that there is no life on Mars. I think that would not be scientific conclusion.

On the other hand, I think one can say it looks like these two sites are more hostile than we had anticipated. It appears that the surface contains very excited chemicals that are giving us a lot of trouble in terms of how we interpret the Viking data. But that could all be sort of a blind alley we're going down and it just may be we don't have the right experiments or the right conditions to pick up signs of biology on Mars.

My feeling is we'll not be able to prove any more until we go back to Mars. I know that a lot of people will be doing lab work to try to understand what might be happening, but even if people come up with good models, they will never prove what is happening on Mars. I feel we will either have to go back, if we want to settle that question, or bring samples back.

The lander II soil sampler collector arm successfully pushed a rock at left several inches from its original position October 8, 1976. At right, a soil sample from beneath the rock was delivered to the organic chemistry instrument to determine if life existed beneath rocks sheltered from the Sun's ultraviolet radiation. The test proved negative.

Search for Organics

The gas chromatograph mass spectometer instrument performed organic chemical analyses of the Martian soil and analyzed the components of the Martian atmosphere at the surface. This experiment had the potential to reveal any existence of past life on the planet.

In terms of instrument performance, qualitatively and quantitatively, both objectives were met. The loss of one of three ovens on each of the landers limited the number of soil samples to two per lander, but the loss was not a detriment to the instrument's performance. The primary mission activities consisted of 39 atmospheric samplings and a multiple analysis of four soil samples, two samples per lander.

The atmospheric analyses revealed the following compositions in comparison with the Earth:

ATMOSPHERIC COMPOSITION
EARTH/MARS COMPARISON

Element	Mars	Earth
Carbon Dioxide	96%	0.03%
Nitrogen	2.5%	78%
Oxygen	0.1%	21%
Argon 40	1.5%	0.9%
Argon 36	4 ppm	32 ppm
Krypton	< 0.9 ppm	1 ppm
Xenon		^{129}Xe enhanced relative to other Xe isotopes on Mars compared to Earth values

The amount of nitrogen on Mars indicates that there should be much, much more water than exists in the atmosphere. There is about a thousand times more nitrogen on Earth than on Mars. The Mars atmosphere is one percent N_2 and Earth's is 80% N_2.

On Earth there is a certain amount of water relative to the amount of nitrogen. Comparing these ratios with Mars, there should be approximately one percent of the water we have on Earth. Everybody believes that if the water does exist on Mars in the quantity indicated, it is underground.

Aside from the confirmation of the presence of nitrogen, the next most interesting finding was the determination of the ratio of argon 36 to argon 40. The ratio on Mars is one in three thousand atoms, as contrasted to one in three hundred on Earth, which means 10 times more argon 40 with respect to argon 36 is present on Mars than on Earth. Argon 40 was found to be no more than 2 percent of the atmosphere by volume. The noble gases provide a useful measure of the degree of outgassing a planet has undergone because they cannot be cycled in and out of the atmosphere by chemical combination. The gases still present show the path of the planet's evolution. One possible theoretical consequence of the argon ratio is that Mars has not outgassed to the extent the Earth has, and that its atmospheric pressure may never have exceeded 100 millibars.

Molecular Analysis Team: Klaus Biemann (Team Leader), Massachusetts Institute of Technology; Duwayne Anderson, Earth Sciences Branch, Cold Regions Research & Engineering Lab; Alfred O.C. Nier, School of Physics and Astronomy, University of Minnesota; Leslie E. Orgel, Senior Resident Fellow, The Salk Institute for Biological Studies; John Oro, Department of Biophysical Sciences, University of Houston; Tobias Owen, State University of New York, Department of Earth and Space Sciences; Priestley Toulmin, III, U.S. Geological Survey; and Harold C. Urey, University Professor Emeritus, Chemistry Department, University of California at San Diego.

Dr. Klaus Biemann

A search for organic compounds on the surface of Mars was conducted to find out whether compounds consisting of carbon, hydrogen, nitrogen and oxygen existed on the surface of the planet. In a nut shell, the result was that we did not find organic compounds at the level of a few parts per billion with respect to the soil material.

To put that in perspective, we could have detected something like a hundred or thousand times less organic materials than contained in typical antarctic soil, which is low in organic compounds because there is little vegetation and animal life in that part of our planet.

Compared to this source, Mars is devoid of organic material and a number of conclusions can be drawn from that finding. First, there is no synthesis of organic compounds presently occurring on the surface. Second, if in the past history of the planet, millions of years ago, organic compounds would have been formed, they seem to have since been destroyed. Third, since organic compounds must be arriving on Mars in the form of meteorites, one must assume that the material either has been imbedded in the Martian surface very deeply and is therefore highly diluted or, more likely, it does not survive for a long period of time in the harsh environment on the surface of the planet. The high intensity of ultraviolet radiation on the surface may decompose organic compounds within a reasonable period of time. Finally, if we use terrestrail analogies, we always find that a large amount of organic material accompanies living things a hundred times, thousand times, 10 thousand times more organic materials than the cells themselves represent.

Since we didn't find that large amount of organic waste material, it is difficult to see how micro-organisms could be living at the areas we investigated if they behave as terrestrial organisms do. This does not rule out a different kind of living mechanism that would protect its organic constituents very well and, therefore, avoid this waste of a scarce commodity.

Perhaps Martian organisms have evolved along those lines and, while the environment got harsher and harsher, have become more and more efficeint in utilizing the organic materials they need and that spill out when the cells die.

In the experiment, we also found that water is incorporated in the surface minerals. When we heated the samples to 660 or 930° F, a few tenths of a percent in weight of the sample came off as water. It cannot just be absorbed on the surface, like wet material. Therefore, it must be a mineral hydrate that decomposes on heating. This has more implications for the mineralogy and inorganic chemistry investigations of the surface materials than for organic chemistry.

Of course, we have looked at only two samples for each of the two landing sites at depths reaching to 5 to 10 centimeters at the very most. If, for example, organic materials were produced millions or hundreds of millions of years ago, they could be present at greater depths and protected there from the ultraviolet radiation. We may be sitting on an area a few meters down, containing a deposit of organic material that we are not able to dig down to. There also could be other areas on the planet where the surface material is more protected or where organic material is presently being synthesized and not destroyed.

In the future we plan to study the rate of decomposition of certain, typical organic compounds under Martian conditions to see how fast organic materials would be destroyed at the surface.

The second aspect of the molecular analysis experiment involves a repetitive analysis of the composition of the atmosphere at the surface. The atmosphere had been analyzed by the entry team's mass spectrometer during the descent of the spacecraft at higher altitudes.

After landing, we used our mass spectrometer to repetitively analyze the atmosphere. The major constituent, carbon dioxide, is removed by a chemical method thus enriching the minor constituents that are then analyzed. In that way we were able to determine the isotopic ratios of the noble gases — argon, krypton and xenon.

The isotopic ratio of nitrogen is 1 to 165, i.e., one ^{15}N atom (heavy nitrogen) for every 165 ^{14}N atoms (normal nitrogen). On earth, the ratio is one ^{15}N atom to about 277 ^{14}N atoms. The argon 36 to 40 ratio is one in 3000 compared to one in 300 on Earth, which means there is 10 times more argon 40 on Mars relative to argon 36 then on Earth. Argon 40 is produced by radioactive decomposition of potassium 40 and therefore is of a different origin than argon 36. To determine the argon concentrations in the original atmosphere, one has to use argon 36 rather than the total argon concentration. The krypton isotopic ratio is about as it is on Earth, and so is the argon 36-to-Krypton ratio, but the total amount is about 100 times less. The xenon falls in the same category; it is of the same relative abundance as on Earth except that the isotopic composition is also somewhat different. Mars has about 2.5 times as much xenon 129 compared to the other xenon isotopes as the Earth. Again xenon 129 stems from the radioactive isotope of iodine 129 and therefore is not a cosmic isotope.

From these data, we can draw some analogies to say that the noble gases represent a measure of the total original atmosphere, and even that involves the assumption that the Earth has the same amount of noble gases as Mars. Then one comes to the conclusion that Mars now has about 100 times less atmosphere than it ought to have — the question then is "Where did the atmosphere go?"

The McElroy (Dr. Michael McElroy, Harvard University) depletion model would predict a loss of atmosphere by a factor of 10 and the question is whether that is enough. Much of the carbon dioxide may be locked up in the surface material of the planet since we now know that the residual polar caps are water-ice and not frozen carbon dioxide. Alternatively, Mars may just never have produced as much atmosphere as the Earth. Which one of those answers, or any combination thereof, would be an adequate explanation of the present situation? We do not know as yet, but the results of these and other Viking experiments will bring us much closer to the answer.

Martian Weather

The meteorology instrument was designed to measure atmospheric pressure, temperature, wind speed and wind direction. The data were then compared with landing site and orbital photography to understand the Martian atmosphere and weather.

The meteorology instrument performed perfectly until the 46th Martian day for lander I when an open connection to the heater power circuit was discovered, causing the quadrant heater to fail. Computer techniques were developed to compensate for this failure so wind data could still be obtained. A temperature sensor on lander II also developed problems. Again a computer study was used to work around the problem.

More than a year after landing, both instruments still recorded essential weather information for study by meteorology experts on Earth.

Meteorology Team: Seymour L. Hess (Team Leader), Department of Meteorology, Florida State University; Robert M. Henry, Langley Research Center; Conway Leovy, Department of Atmospheric Sciences, University of Washington; John Ryan, Earth Sciences Department, California State University, Fullerton; and James E. Tillman, Department of Atmospheric Sciences, University of Washington.

Dr. Seymour L. Hess

We found two startling things in the meteorology experiment. One is the extreme uniformity of the variations through a Martian day of the weather eleements we measured, namely the pressure, the temperature, the wind speed and the wind direction. For a long, long time during the mission, each day's results were very much like the previous day's results. That, we believe, is because the Martian atmosphere is much simpler than Earth's atmosphere because of the very, very small amount of water vapor and the complete absence of oceans. All the water in the Earth's atmosphere and on its surface contributes substantially to the variability of the weather from day to day that is absent on Mars. Of course, in the early part of the mission it was summertime in the northern part of the hemisphere and in summertime things tend to be more uniform even here on Earth.

The second startling discovery was the seasonal variation of pressure. When we first landed, we detected a steady decrease in the mean pressure from day to day. In our early publications, we attributed that to condensation of carbon dioxide on the winter cap in the southern hemisphere, removing a major constituent from the atmosphere at a certain rate resulting in the change in the pressure.

Now in the extended mission we have seen the pressure at both landers reach its lowest value on a seasonal basis and begin to rise again. It's now back up to where it was when we first landed and we are quite sure we are seeing the consequences of condensation of carbon dioxide on the winter cap and its release as spring comes to the northern hemisphere.

The importance of the first point, the uniformity of the patterns from day to day, is that it confirms our theoretical expectations of what we would find when we got there. If confirms the idea that the Martian atmosphere is a more simple version of the Earth's atmosphere.

That, of course, is a very important idea in that it continues to give us hope that what we learn from Viking can be brought back and applied to the atmosphere of the Earth. If we have the opportunity to study a simple case, we can hardly fail to improve our understanding of the more complex case. That's one of the basic reasons why some of us were involved in Viking.

The second point is important for a variety of reasons. First of all because it means that a measurement made at only two locations is telling us what's happening planetwide. This is an observation that's not limited in its applicability to the two locations at which we happened to land. It's telling us something about how the pressure is varying seasonally over the entire planet. It's telling us something about the rate at which carbon dioxide condenses on, and is released from, the polar caps.

When we have still more of the seasonal curve, we will make a detailed comparison of the observations with the theories as to what is happening to the carbon dioxide. One theory is that there is merely an exchange of carbon dioxide between the caps and the atmosphere. A second theory says that there is also adsorption of carbon dioxide on the regolith or soil making it a three-cornered affair — atmosphere, poles, and soil. We want to distinguish between the two cases and determine whether there is an appreciable amount of adsorption on the soil.

One of the other things that Viking showed is that the temperature of the residual northern polar cap in summer was too high to be carbon dioxide. It has to be water-ice. Until Viking landed, the evidence that we saw for climate change on Mars was tentatively explained in terms of a fairly substantial reservoir of carbon dioxide in the residual summer polar cap, and that nature could cook out this carbon dioxide and add it to the atmosphere because of changes in the inclination of the planet. To change the climate on Mars and have more water in the atmosphere and on the surface, you have to have a more massive atmosphere. The polar cap was presumed to be the reservoir, but we now know that it isn't.

So where is the reservoir? The only place left to act as a reservoir of carbon dioxide is adsorption of carbon dioxide on the soil. We are gathering data that can contribute to our understanding of whether such adsorption takes place significantly or not. If it isn't adsorbed on the soil, I don't know where it is.

At the Viking II site, which is at 48° north, the temperatures dropped pretty much as expected as we entered the Martian winter. Early in the mission, we had minimum temperatures of about -125°F. During the winter we were getting minimum temperatures just about dawn of -180°F.

The condensation point of carbon dioxide is about -190° F. Frost on the surface was first observed in mid-September 1977. At the time, lander II was recording nighttime temperatures of -171° F and the photo of the frost was taken at -144° F, which is inconsistent with carbon dioxide frost formation. However, thermal mapping and water vapor instruments on the Viking orbiter indicated temperatures were lower than measured by the lander, suggesting that the frost is carbon dioxide rather than water frost.

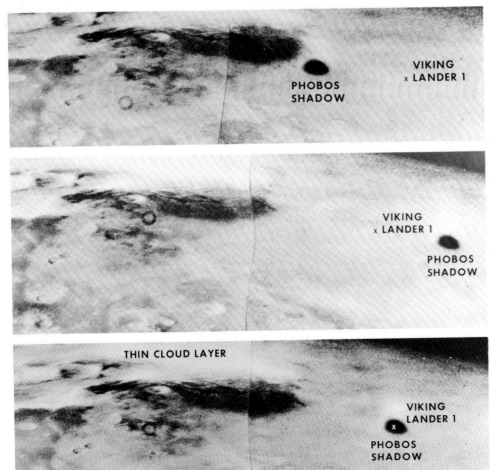

Orbiter I recorded the shadow of Phobos, one of the Martian moons, moving eastward across thin clouds near the surface in an experiment that pinpointed the position of lander I within 650 feet. The shadow is 56 miles long and is shown moving about 220 miles across the surface from west to east. The crater Sharanov at upper left is 93 miles in diameter.

With the winter, the wind speeds increased slightly, especially at the Viking II site, with several interruptions in what had been a regular pattern of wind direction. Then we had several periods of northerly winds all day for several days in a row associated with temporary drops in temperature. The presumption is that we saw passages of cold fronts. We had thought winter, and the fallout of carbon dioxide, would cause a drastic increase in wind speeds and variability. There have been some wind directional changes and gusts, but no noticeable changes or patterns in wind direction or speed as of October 1977.

It is particularly significant that we have measured the average variation of pressure during the day on Mars. These daily changes are caused by solar heating and also occur on Earth. There is a complex theory to explain these changes on Earth, and Viking represents our first opportunity to test the theory on another planet.

There are two components to this variation of pressure we have been able to measure on Mars. The theory says that one of these components should be strongly affected by the distribution of land and sea and of mountains, while the second component should be largely independent of these features. Mars has no seas and has a very different distribution of mountains than Earth. Therefore the first component should be different on Mars, while the second component should look just like its counterpart on Earth. Both these implications are verified by the Viking measurements.

The point is that we meteorologists have never before had the opportunity to check our theories on anything other than Earth's atmosphere. Now Viking has provided a second case and we can place more confidence in our theories when they are verified on Mars. This process has been called "comparative planetology," and is a very important motivation for exploration of the planets.

A global scale dust storm is nearly covering Mars' southern hemisphere in this photo. The storm was believed to have begun several days before orbiter II took the photo. The 27-frame mosaic was shot from a distance of 16,740 miles showing two of the large Tharsis volcanoes at the upper left as dark circular markings. The Valles Marineris canyon system stretches across the top frames just north of the mass of storm clouds. Dark areas within the clouds are clear spots allowing the planet to show through.

The Frozen Planet

The water vapor mapping investigation was designed to map the distribution of water vapor over the planet and to determine the pressure of the atmosphere at the level where the vapor is present. Understanding the distribution of water vapor on Mars is crucial to understanding the geological features of the planet and the possibility of the existence of life. The instruments located aboard the orbiters are capable of measuring water vapor to an accuracy of one precipitable micrometer of water.

One of the more significant contributions of the investigation was to help determine that the polar ice cap was water-ice rather than carbon dioxide-ice as had been thought. This was important to the theories on climatic change that were put forward prior to Viking. Those findings were based on the potential release of large quantities of carbon dioxide as the catalyst for climatic change.

Another surprise was that the total amount of water vapor has hardly changed even though it has undergone a radical redistribution. The Viking results show the planet has not lost its original water supply. The total atmospheric water vapor is equivalent to an ice cube more than one-fourth a cubic mile. In comparison, while the water vapor on Earth determines the weather, on Mars there isn't enough to affect the weather so the weather determines the water vapor.

The Mars studies turned out to be useful because of the similarity between the Earth's stratosphere and the Mars atmosphere. Scientists hope to learn more about the motions of the Earth's atmosphere and about its photochemistry through direct comparison with Mars.

Water Vapor Mapping Team: C. Barney Farmer (Team Leader), Jet Propulsion Laboratory; Dan D. Laporte, Santa Barbara Research Center; and Donald W. Davies, Jet Propulsion Laboratory.

Dr. C. Barney Farmer

We have been monitoring the behavior of the water vapor in the Mars atmosphere for more than a year. We have been able to follow its variations with time of day, location, elevation and latitude and have begun to observe how these characteristics change with season.

The most important fundamental questions we hope to be able to answer with the Viking observations concern the sources and sinks of the planet's present water vapor — "Where is the water stored and what mechanisms control the seasonal behavior of the vapor phase?" During the primary mission, the water vapor underwent a gradual redistribution, the latitude of the maximum amounts moving from the north polar toward the equator. One of the most interesting results was that during this time, while the amounts of vapor at some latitudes changed dramatically, the total global water vapor remained almost constant at the equivalent of about 1 cubic kilometer of ice. The largest amounts we have observed thus far were found over the dark polar region, a region not previously studied since it was inaccessible to Earth-based observers. Maximum vapor column abundances of about 100 precipitable microns were measured adjacent to the residual cap itself — a very large amount considering the temperature of the surface and atmosphere in this region.

The results led to the conclusion that the residual cap is made of water-ice and that the atmosphere above it is saturated with vapor during the polar summer. The fact that the small permanent cap is water-ice rather than solid carbon dioxide, as many had thought prior to Viking has important consequences in terms of the theories put forward suggesting periodic climatic changes in which the Martian atmosphere could become dense and warm enough to support the survival of large bodies of liquid water, even to the extent there could be rainstorms. These theories were attractive in that they conveniently explained the numerous channels that appear to have been formed by flowing water. It is now felt to be more probable that the channels, if they were in fact formed by flowing water, resulted from singular events that occurred during the planet's early history rather than from periodic climate changes.

We might add that we have carried out some initial analysis of the polar results and conclude that the residual ice is dirty — that is, it is mixed with dust and is not very much brighter than the bright areas of Mars away from the poles. It is probable that the formation, appearance and composition of the surface ice and dust mixture is very dependent on the severity of the dust storm activity during the previous few seasons.

Although we have not yet been able to determine the thickness of the ice, estimates based on several different factors indicate its minimum thickness is between a few meters and a kilometer.

Although we must await analysis of the results from a larger fraction of the Mars year than we have covered so far, we can draw tentative conclusions regarding the relationship between the atmospheric vapor and the surface or subsurface ice. The global observations to date are consistent with the existence of a reservoir of water in the form of ice buried beneath the surface. In other words, as the seasons change, more or less water is observed in the atmosphere depending on the temperature. When the water is less in the atmosphere, it has returned to the surface or subsurface until, with a seasonal change in temperature, it returns again to the atmosphere. This, of course, does not *prove* the existence of a reservoir of ice, or of permafrost, but the evidence strongly suggests that the planet has not lost the bulk of its primordial water.

Orbiter I's two TV cameras captured Argyre Planitia, well known to telescope observers as an area of occasional clouds. The four-frame picture shows the horizon 12,000 miles away and was taken from a range of over 11,000 miles. The detached layers of clouds are 15 to 25 miles high and are thought to be crystals of carbon dioxide. The heavily cratered terrain is surrounded by a smooth plain and is located 50° south of the equator.

-225° F

The function of the infrared thermal mapper on the orbiter is to determine the surface and atmospheric temperatures of Mars, map their variations, determine the temperature of any frost or clouds, and investigate the nature of any condensation of moisture.

Mounted on the orbiter scan platform, the mapper measures the infrared brightness of the surface temperatures, composition and roughness and allows scientists to accurately translate these radiation measurements into surface and cloud temperatures.

Mars was found to have temperature patterns similar in size to continents on Earth, which scientists have termed continental scale weather. In theory, the temperature patterns may be associated with cloud patterns. At the extreme, the temperature shows a very wide variation on a daily basis. The typical day-night variation on Earth is 10 to 20° F, on Mars the temperature will move from near -207° F to near 44° F. The atmospheric density was found to be changing by a factor of two on a daily basis.

An important contribution of the experiment toward uncovering the history of the planet is the impact on the idea of how much volatile material has outgassed throughout the Martian history. The mapper also helped with another important discovery on the nature of the polar ice cap — while scientists had once thought it to be carbon dioxide-ice, Viking has proved it to be water-ice.

Thermal Mapping Team: Hugh H. Kieffer (Team Leader), Department of Planetary and Space Science, University of California; Stillman Chase, Santa Barbara Research Center; Ellis Miner, Member Technical Staff, Jet Propulsion Laboratory; Guido Munch, Professor, Department of Astronomy, California Institute of Technology; Gerry Neugebauer, Professor, Department of Physics, California Institute of Technology; and Frank Don Palluconi, Jet Propulsion Laboratory.

Dr. Hugh H. Kieffer

We had suspected that Mars would have a certain set of thermal properties and had made some predictions about the temperature over the entire planet. On the average these predictions are correct, with some notable exceptions.

One exception is that in the winter the polar regions become considerably colder than we had expected. Temperatures drop below the freezing point for carbon dioxide at the polar surface on Mars. The temperature dropped as low as -225° F near the geometric pole in the middle of winter. This may be caused by the atmosphere freezing out most of its carbon dioxide locally so the atmospheric composition becomes predominantly argon, nitrogen and oxygen. This process of having a very major change in atmospheric composition does not occur on the Earth. It is a process that could be studied with some interest by a return mission to Mars.

Another behavior of the planet that leaves us slightly confused is the tendency of the temperatures in the afternoon to drop much more quickly than expected. What we've found for several regions on Mars is that toward the middle of the afternoon the temperatures begin to drop more rapidly than predicted until just before dusk. They may be 20 to 30 degrees cooler than we had expected for that time. Then the temperatures cease to drop so rapidly and slowly merge with the predictions for the evening. In the afternoon the only atmospheric regions that are cooler than the surface are very high and thus we don't know what process at the moment is causing this rapid surface cooling. It may be related to clouds in some way, but most of the atmosphere near the ground, were one expects clouds to form, is, in fact, warmer than the surface just before sunset.

Another thing we've found is that there appear to be large patterns in the temperature of Mars on the scale similar to the size of continents on the Earth. These may be associated with cloud patterns. It's possible we're seeing what I call continental scale weather. The temperatures shortly before dawn in some places are much cooler than we expected. In other areas, for instance over the Vallas Marinaras, temperatures are quite warm just before dawn. The temperatures just before dawn are more directly related to the physical properties of the surface because there is no solar energy being absorbed during the 12 hours of night. This means the temperatures are a good indication of how well the surface can hold its heat.

In the extreme, the temperatures show a wide variation on a daily basis. On Earth, in a typical temperate climate, a day-night variation is on the order of 10 or perhaps 20 degrees. On Mars we're

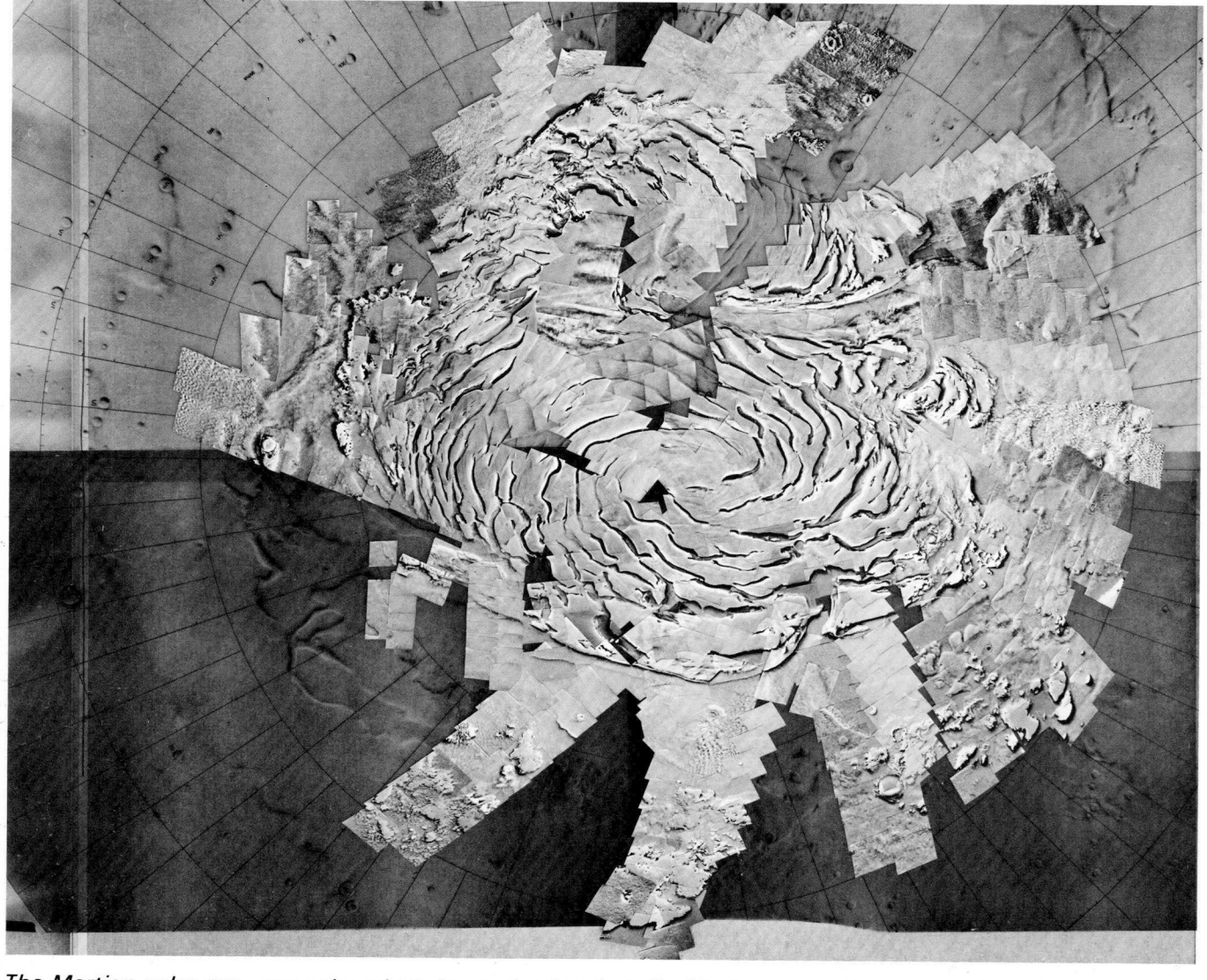

The Martian polar cap, once thought to be made of carbon dioxide, has proved to be water ice. Prior evidence pointed to carbon dioxide, however, when the polar cap retreated in midsummer it left a smaller glacier behind. The temperatures of this residual polar cap show it could not be carbon dioxide, but had to be water frost. The scarp is apparently an erosional feature. The variety of arc-shaped cliffs illustrates the complexity of erosion in the north polar region.

finding some places, particularly near the summits of the large volcanoes, where the surface temperatures are changing from near -207° F to near 44° F (140 to 280 K) every day. Thus far we know only that the surface temperatures, and presumably the temperatures of the atmosphere near the ground, undergo these large changes. The atmospheric pressure near the ground also is changing by a factor of two on a daily basis. This creates the possibility of some very unusual dynamic meteorology at the volcanoes, extending well up into the atmosphere. The large density change in the atmosphere might create very strong drainage winds during the night — with winds blowing back up the slopes of the volcanoes during

the day. Again this process is of a magnitude much greater than anything we have on Earth.

One of the major questions posed by Mariner IX was the composition of the residual polar cap. We have known for some time that the winter polar cap is made of frozen carbon dioxide but when it retreated in midsummer, a small polar cap remained. A major controversy existed over whether this summer cap was also frozen carbon dioxide or frozen water. Now, thanks to Viking, we know the temperatures of the residual polar cap in the north during midsummer to latesummer are near -90 to -81° F, showing that it could not be carbon dioxide but had to be water frost.

Also the brightness of the frost indicates it has a lot of dirt mixed in with it. The dirty nature of the ice has also been seen now by the orbital imaging system.

So it appears there is no permanent reservoir of carbon dioxide in the polar regions of Mars and the possibility of a rapid climate change induced by the instability of the carbon dioxide seems to be gone. This means we still don't have an adequate explanation of how the atmosphere could have been of sufficient density to sustain the liquid water that appears to have flowed at one time in streams and rivers on the surface of Mars.

The Viking thermal mapper was designed primarily to be a surface mapping experiment. We had expected to do our analysis primarily just considering the surface behavior in temperature, but we have found that the atmosphere has a much larger effect on the temperatures and on the reflected brightnesses than we expected. That has been a surprise to us and has very much complicated analyzing the data. The magnitude of the variations was much larger than we had expected. It's very interesting. We had not expected such low temperatures at the pole. We had not expected the enormous temperature changes. We've seen evidence of clouds where the temperatures on one particular day might be 30 to 40 degrees cooler than on another day.

It's clear that the models we developed from Mariner IX, in which the temperature depended only on the time of day, the latitude and the time of year, are not really adequate because there are weather patterns

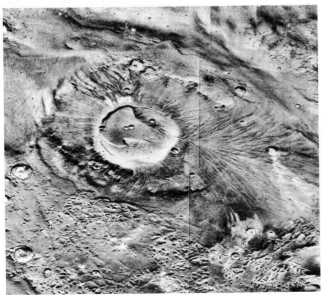

Martian volcano Appolineris Patera, one of the oldest volcanoes, was photographed from 4,600 miles by orbiter I. It is 62 miles wide.

coming through that effect the surface. The big uncertain factor is how much the weather variations are affecting our measurements and how badly our predictions might be off if the weather patterns change and they do change. Initially, we saw an unusually clear atmosphere in the northern summer and since then, in the Viking extended mission, the atmosphere has become cloudy over much of the planet.

In terms of the planetary evolution, there are at least two ways our experiment might make a contribution. One would be if we happened to find an area that indicated there were still active volcanisms. This would be a place warmer than could result from absorbed sunlight. That would be an extremely lucky find because it would take a very large area of volcanic activity for us to see it. We have not seen it, but the possibility exists.

The other area where I believe we have influenced the thoughts about the way Mars evolved is the fact that the residual polar cap is water. The water vapor experiment has shown that there is an abundance of water in the atmosphere. The polar regions, and probably the subsurface over much of the planet, are saturated with water. The puzzle is the absence of solid carbon dioxide at the polar caps. In a sense, we are worse off than we were before Viking with this continued conflict between the surface features and the current atmosphere.

I think there is now a stronger incentive to look for other places on the planet where materials that could contribute to the atmosphere are somehow bound up in the surface. One possibility is that a lot of carbon dioxide is physically absorbed. That is, individual molecules bound to the grains of the soil. We don't know at the moment how much carbon dioxide might be bound up that way.

In summary, I think our major contribution toward the history of the planet is our impact on the idea of how much volatile material there is and how much material has outgassed throughout Martian history. I also anticipate that the measurement of surface properties and some mapping of geologic units will affect the ideas of the geologic history of the surface, but I don't know how yet. At the moment I'm inclined to think that our major contribution will ultimately be instigating a new study of dynamical meteorology; we've found at least two types of thermal behavior and probably atmospheric dynamics that are extreme compared to the Earth and therefore will take a more intensive study than possible with current theories. By trying to understand these extreme examples of atmospheric behavior, we may gain some insight into the more complex, but not so extreme, cases that occur on the Earth.

100,000,000-Year-Old Floods

Dr. Michael H. Carr

The tasks set for the orbiter camera were to aid in the selection of a safe and scientifically interesting landing site for the lander, to observe large-scale features of the landing sites for correlation with lander data from the surface, to observe and map the planet for subsequent study of the geologic features and to investigate the atmosphere of Mars.

Mars' geological history shows evidence of floods and relatively recent volcanic eruptions, at least in the hundreds of million years that geology uses as a measure. There are also features that resemble terrestrial river systems. Apparently enormous floods occurred many times over Mars' history, indicating the planet must have been drastically different in the past.

The plains regions, originally thought to be formed by fissure eruptions, appear to be formed from the lava of large volcanoes that have spread over the plains probably a billion years ago. Some flows have traveled several hundred kilometers implying a low viscosity and a rock rich in minerals and iron. The volcanoes and the plains around them appear to be young in terms of Martian history.

The presence of a permafrost layer also was picked up by the cameras. The layers resemble glaciers on Earth with evidence that suggests the permafrost covers most of the planet.

By October 1977, orbiter I had taken 7966 pictures and orbiter II had taken 8124 for a total of 16,090. The orbiters continued to take as many as 60 pictures each day.

Orbiter Imaging Team: Michael H. Carr (Team Leader), Branch of Astrogeologic Studies, U.S. Geological Survey; William Baum, Planetary Research Center, Lowell Observatory; Geoffrey Briggs, Jet Propulsion Laboratory; James A. Cutts, Science Applications, Inc.; Harold Masursky, Center of Astrogeology, U.S. Geological Survey; and Don Wise, Department of Geology, University of Massachusetts.

The orbiter imaging data were expected to significantly add to our understanding of the geology of Mars, particularly our ability to date things, to put things in their relative sequence by means of crater counts. Higher resolution pictures enable you to look at smaller features. Because the number of impact craters increases dramatically with decreasing size, the effectiveness of the technique, the precision with which you can do the relative dating, is dramatically increased with better resolution. Since acquiring the data, we have been doing crater counts on many different kinds of features and are now beginning to place things in their relative sequence.

The volcanic features have been somewhat of a surprise. We thought we pretty well knew what the history of Martian volcanism was before the Viking mission, but I think there has been a major surprise particularly in the Tharsis area. For one thing, the plains around Tharsis, which were formerly thought to be formed by fissure eruptions, now appear to be formed by lavas largely derived from the large volcanoes themselves that have spread out over the plains. Some of the flows appear to have gone for distances of several hundred kilometers, which implies a very low viscosity and probably a rock very rich in dark minerals and probably very iron-rich. This is required to give the very low viscosities implied by the very long lava flows.

We have done crater counts on these flows and they turn out to be dramatically lower than counts almost anywhere else on the planet. This indicates the plains around the large volcanoes and the volcanoes themselves are quite young in terms of Martian history. They range in age by a factor of about 20. That is, it appears that the flows close to the large volcanoes are a factor of 20 times younger than those at the edge of the plateau. It looks as though the many large Tharsis volcanoes have been accumulating over a very long period of time, right up to the recent geologic past or, in effect, up to the present.

We've looked at other features on the planet, such as channel features or plains or canyons, made counts and tried to compare them with what we're observing

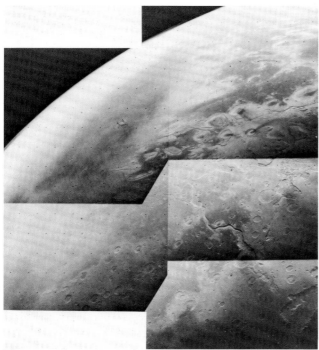

The mosaic was acquired while orbiter I was near its orbital highpoint of 20,000 miles. Ganges Chasm, lower right, is the canyon that leads into Valles Marineris complex, some of which is visible along the right edge of the mosaic. The white patch near Ganges is thought to be water-ice fog very close to the surface.

in the Tharsis region. In general we're finding everything else is older. It looks as though during the last half of the planet's history volcanics were accumulating in the Tharsis region but there wasn't much else going on at least in the part of the planet. That was a surprise.

The channels themselves are one of the big puzzles on Mars. What are the channels? How do they form? We have been doing a lot of work in this area and essentially there are two major kinds. There are the large flood features and then there are dendritic or branching drainage features that resemble terrestrial river systems. It appears from the crater counts that the fine terrestrial-like river channel systems are older than the flood features. It appears that the large flood features came in middle Mars history. There was a period of vast floods, then the flooding for some reason ceased or became less frequent because we don't have flood features with crater counts comparable to those we find on the Tharsis volcanoes. Very early in Mars history, dendritic drainage patterns developed; in Mars' middle history it had a period of flooding, and then mostly after that the volcanics of Tharsis accumulated. This general picture has come out of the Viking data.

A lot of skeptics didn't believe there had been any period of surface drainage. Some said all those things could easily have been formed by faulting and so on. The Viking pictures are full of examples of dendritic channels. I can't believe there are many skeptics left. I think we have really established that there was this early period of surface drainage. There can be very little doubt about that.

Another topic is permafrost. To me one of the more exciting things we've observed is the abundant evidence of permafrost. The most striking features indicative of permafrost occur along the edge of old crater terrain. We see what appears to be large debris flows that resemble features seen on Earth in glacial regions. They form by mass movement of surface material probably aided by the freezing and thawing of ground ice. Another possible indicator of ground ice is the unique character of material ejected from impact craters on Mars that is quite different from the pattern on the Moon and on Mercury. We interpret the difference as due to ground ice on Mars. The impact melts the ground ice and lubricates the ejector that is thrown out of the crater so when it lands on the ground it flows away from the crater in a debris flow and forms the characteristic features we have observed.

We also have evidence of permafrost from the large landslides. The most plausible explanation of the very large landslides we see in the canyons is that they are caused by the decreasing strength of the materials in the canyon walls through the sublimation of ice. Many of the features of the large channels, the flood features especially, indicate water came out of the

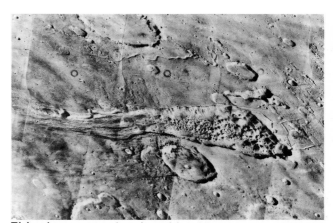

This photo was taken by orbiter I from a range of 1400 miles covering an area about 180 miles square. The top of the photo shows signs of flooding while in the foreground is a valley, probably caused by downfaulting of the Mars crust although it has been suggested that the subsidence is partially caused by melting of subsurface ice.

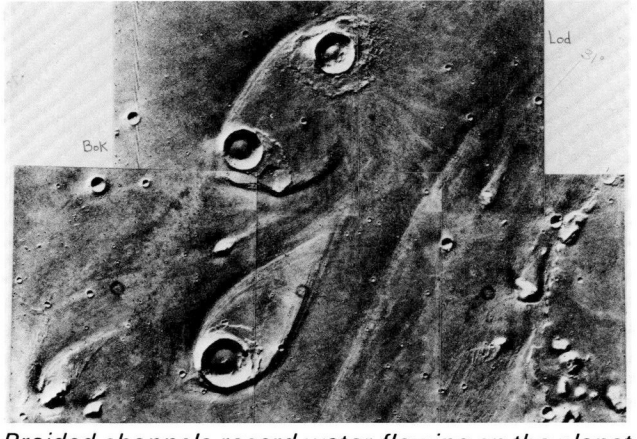

Braided channels record water flowing on the planet in the past in this photo from about 990 miles above the Chryse region near the lander I site. The three larger craters were caused before the flood while the smaller ones followed it.

ground by some mechanism and large amounts may be stored as ground ice. There is, therefore, a lot of evidence that converges to suggest there is extensive permafrost, very thick permafrost, over much of the planet, an observation that will be very important for future missions.

As a result of the better Viking photography, we're getting both a better and a more precise idea of the age and also the mechanism of the formation of the Martian canyons. We're seeing features in the bottom of the canyon that look like faults. It's probable that the canyon was initially formed by faults, but it's also equally clear that secondary processes have worked to undermine the initially formed scarp. Thus, the primary cause of the canyon was faulting and secondary enlargement has taken place as a result of erosion.

Another area for which we have good data is the polar regions. We have excellent photography of the laminated terrain. One thing immediately clear from the photography is that it is very young because there are virtually no craters on it at all. The laminated terrain may reflect cyclical climatic changes and these climatic changes may be related in some way to formation of the channels of the past. The laminated terrain is, however, much, much younger than the channels. All the channels we see have had abundant craters in them probably formed billions of years ago so there's no obvious connection between the laminated terrain and the channels other than they may both result from changes in climate.

I think we have also been surprised by a number of observations of the atmosphere. One very puzzling feature is the recurrence of clouds in the morning in the Memnonia region between the landers, approximately 100 degrees longitude from each. Every morning clouds appear over this one place. It's very

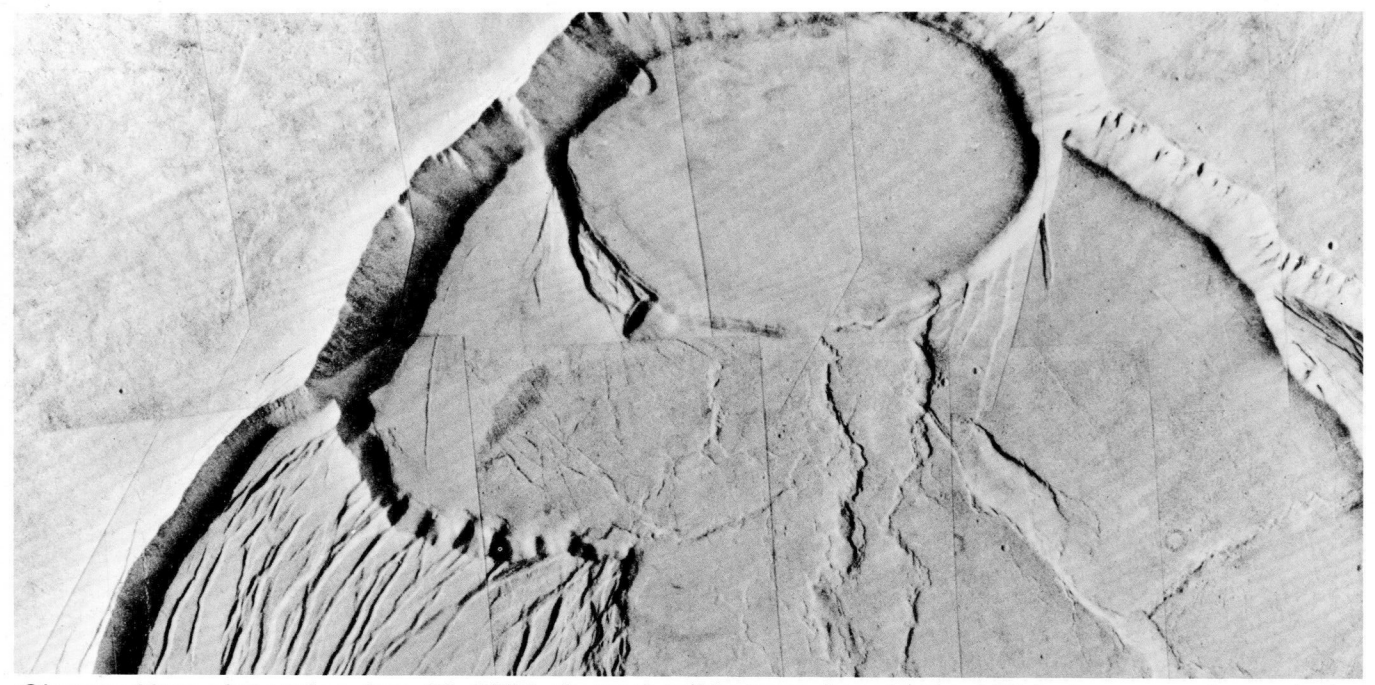

Olympus Mons photo taken June 13, 1977, shows detail features down to about 60 feet across and records the complex features of the summit crater showing a series of eruptions in the form of varied levels of frozen lava lakes. Crater walls are about 1.5 to 1.7 miles tall. Olympus Mons, at 90,000 feet, is the tallest brown mountain in the solar system and is 373 miles across at the base.

This striking photo of the Martian surface and sky was taken from lander II in November, 1976. The color calibration charts are shown in the foreground. Suspended dust particles are the cause of the salmon hue in the sky.

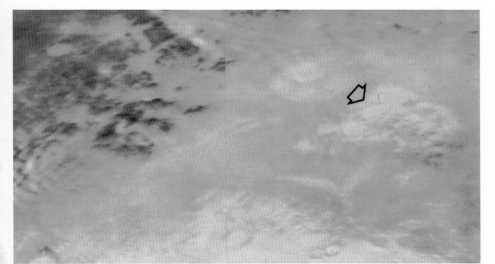

A Martian dust storm in the 1976-1977 Martian winter is shown in this photo from orbiter II. A bright dust cloud (arrow) covering 186 miles of the great Argyre Basin in the southern hemisphere of Mars is apparently moving eastward with strong winds.

"Big Joe", its nearly 7 foot long top covered by fine red dust, stands out on the landscape 26 feet away in this view from lander I.

Many Hues of Mars

Nearly 200 degrees of the Martian horizon at the lander II site can be seen in this composite of three photos taken on three different days, September 4, 5 and 8, 1976. The surface sampler housing is at left and the antenna which receives commands from Earth is at right. The horizon is 1.8 miles from the lander. Dark volcanic rocks can be seen both to the left and right.

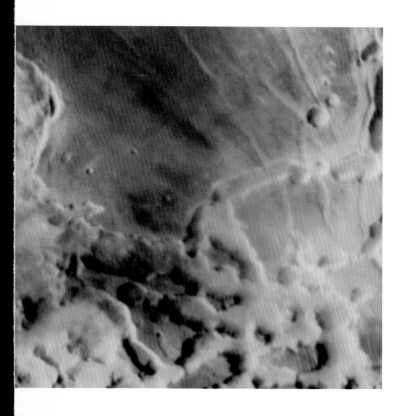

Bright clouds of water-ice can be seen in the tributary canyons as the Sun rises over Noctis Labyrinthus, a high plateau region of Mars. The area seen is about 4000 square miles. The photo was taken by orbiter I on its 40th revolution of the planet.

This dramatic sunset on Mars is captured through infrared filter of the Viking lander I's camera on August 20, 1976. The photo took six minutes to complete, providing the shading effect as sunlight strikes particles in the atmosphere. Red at left is caused by heat from surface rocks.

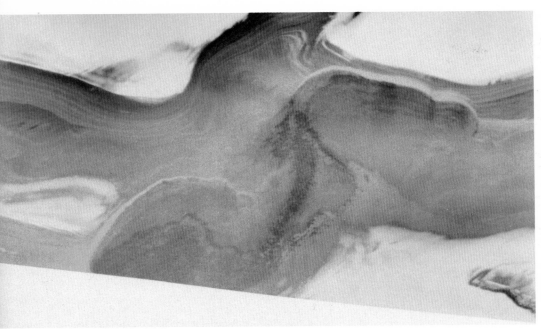

This dramatic scene near the north pole shows the region in midsummer when the seasonal carbon dioxide polar cap clears to reveal water-ice and layered terrain beneath. The variety of arc-shaped cliffs 1640 feet high at the top of the photo illustrates the complexity of erosion in the north polar region.

Deimos, smallest of the Martian satellites, is a uniform gray color, but appears to have tints of orange in the two combined images above taken by orbiter I through a violet filter and an orange filter.

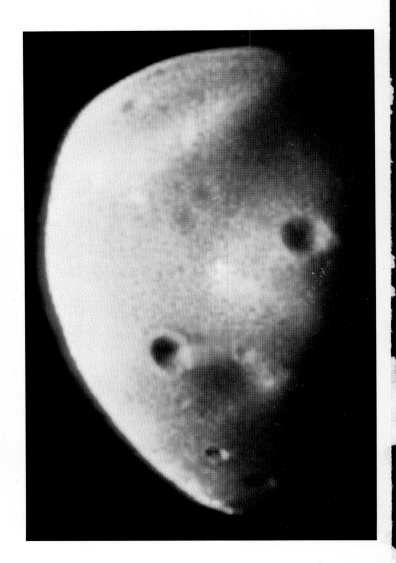

This panorama of the lander I landing area February 19, 1977, shows the trench at right of the metrology boom being dug for soil samples as much as 12 inches below the surface. The unusually bright sky indicates an increase of suspended dust in the atmosphere.

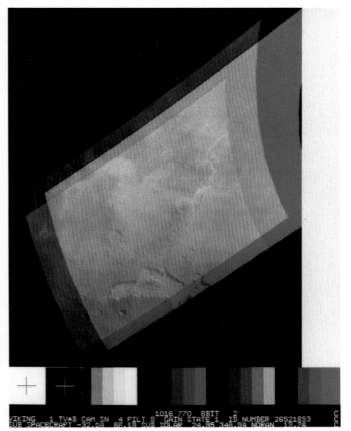

Three separate photos were computer processed to make up this photo of Valles Marineris. They were taken by orbiter I through red, green and violet filters and used to detect color variations that may show compositional mineralogical differences.

This lander II photo shows the first clear indication of frost accumulation on the Martian surface as seen by the lander cameras. This late winter photo shows the white accumulations around the bottom of rocks and scattered patches on the darker surface. Scientists say the frost is most likely carbon dioxide frost due to temperatures recorded by instruments on the orbiter.

The first color photo from Mars taken July 21, 1976, the day following lander I's successful landing on Mars, shows the orange-red surface material that covers most of the planet. Local time was noon.

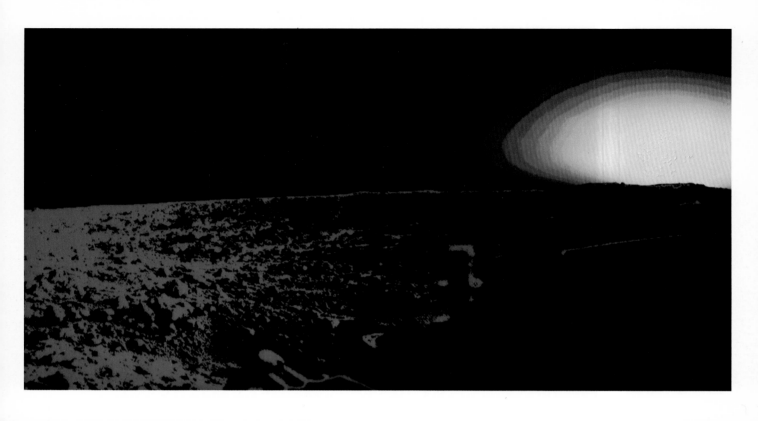

difficult to understand how that can happen. We've also seen clouds that appear about two hours after dawn in low-lying areas that is indicative of some kind of outgassing. If the clouds were to form exclusively as a result of atmospheric conditions, they would be expected to form before dawn when the atmosphere is coldest. What we suspect is happening is that the ground is heating up and driving out water vapor that forms clouds when the vapor hits the cooler parts of the atmosphere above the surface. We've also seen a wide variety of clouds. Normal convective clouds and very disperse clouds appear in the morning, particularly in the Tharsis and Syria regions. One kind of cloud not expected is the extremely high, fast moving cloud we observe close to the morning terminator that appears to be several miles high.

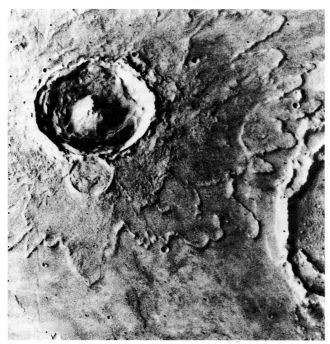

The crater Yuty, 11 miles in diameter with an unusual central peak, probably was formed by the collision of a giant meteorite with the surface of Mars. The flow of material away from the crater is layers of broken rocks thrown out by the shock of impact resembling giant avalanches on earth.

Orbiter I flew within 300 miles of the asteroid-sized Martian moon, Phobos, on February 18, 1977, to take this photo. Phobos is about 13 miles across and 12 miles from top to bottom. Hummocks, seen primarily at the right, are about 165 feet in size and may be debris from previous surface impacts.

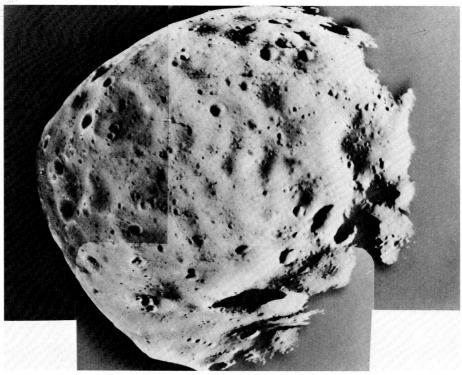

33

View From the Surface

Dr. Thomas Mutch

The main objectives of the lander imaging investigations are to characterize the Martian landscape and its variations, to perform celestial observations and to provide support for other investigations. The photographs record geological detail to help in determining whether past life has existed on Mars. The results aid scientists in understanding the composition and evolution of the Martian surface characteristics.

The cameras also were used to photograph the surface for likely areas for soil sampling. They photographed the soil scooped from the surface allowing the sceintists to compare the images of the soil with similar photographs of terrestrial soil of known composition.

The cameras were operated throughout the lander I and II primary missions. By October 1977, lander I had taken 507 pictures and lander II had taken 1296 for a total of 1803.

Just seconds after lander I touched down on July 20, 1977, camera 2 began photographing the area around footpad 3. It took five minutes of scanning to produce the historic high-resolution photograph. On the first day the camera also acquired a low-resolution panorama view covering 300 degrees of the terrain surrounding the lander. The first color picture was taken on the second Martian day and showed the sky a bright creamy pink.

Throughout the mission the cameras continually operated on both landers without problems.

Lander Imaging Team: Thomas Mutch (Team Leader), Department of Geological Sciences, Brown University; Alan Binder, Science Applications Institute; Friedrich Huck, Langley Research Center; Elliott Levinthal, Department of Genetics, Stanford University; Sidney Liebes, Jr., Department of Genetics, Stanford University; Elliot C. Morris, U.S. Geological Survey; Carl Sagan, Director, Laboratory for Planetary Studies, Center for Radiophysics and Space Research, Cornell University; and James A. Pollack, Ames Research Center.

If you were to tell a geologist that you were going to go out to two places on Earth with your little Brownie to take one or two rolls of film at each locality and then were to come back and from this interpret the history of the planet, he would think you were out of your mind, the most absurd thing he had ever heard of. In a sense it is. So one should not overestimate the exclusive model that you can generate from pictures.

Before you land on a planet, you don't really know whether the terrain is going to be bland or diverse. The pictures from Viking tell us first that the scene is far from bland. A complicated history is exposed there. This is particularly true at the Viking I site, at least it's more obvious there. It may also be true at the Viking lander II site. From a geological point of view, there is clearly a sequence of events represented, probably involving fundamentally different processes — for example, impact, wind, volcanic activity, possibly fluvial activity and possibly ground ice.

At the Viking I site, we have confirmed that there is a diversity of rock types, indicating several petrographic rock types, that is rocks with probably different mineralogy and at least different texture. We suspect that the boulders are more numerous than can be accounted for by impact processes. You have to resort to some other mechanism, either weathering of bed rock or deposition of rocks by fluvial mechanisms. We've seen bed rock. This means that some process either fluvial or alluvial is stripping off the soil to reveal the bed rock. We've seen clear indications of wind. We expected that in one sense, but the wind clearly has formed the dunes and perhaps eroded them somewhat in recent time. The topography at the Viking I site shows ridges trending in two directions, indicating some sort of structural control.

At the Viking II site we see that the rocks are more homogeneous, that is more of one type. They are highly pitted, due either to volcanic vesiculation or to some peculiar erosional process we simply do not understand. While it may run counter to what many other people would say, I think the Viking II site orbital

Lander II's 12 inch foot pad shows an accumulation of sod particles disturbed upon landing.

interpretation is pretty much confirmed by what we see from the surface. I think there's evidence of a wide spread, fine grain sediment mantle at the second lander site. I think we do see the so-called polar mantle. What fools us is that it is littered with boulders and the boulders probably have been super-imposed either as broken lava flows or as ejected boulders from a nearby crater. But we have discovered that the topography at the second lander site is much simpler than at the first lander site. It's a vast plain. And on Earth, plains of that nature are generally alluvial or depositional in nature. Finally, at the Viking II site I think that polygonal trenches may reflect creation of ground ice and permafrost features from some former time.

The analysis of the atmosphere with imaging data is essentially more elegant than geological analysis. It's easier to get a handle on. We have confirmed that the optical depth is much greater than formerly anticipated. This means that there are some scattering and absorbing materials in the lower atmosphere that are almost certainly soil particles. While the existence of soil particles during dust storms have been widely suspected, the existence of fine grain particles more or less as a continuous phenomenon had not been anticipated. The optical depth is greater in the morning than in the afternoon, suggesting the early morning formation of ice crystal clouds when the temperatures are lower. We have recently seen that the optical depth is going way up at the second lander site. It was initially lower at that landing site. We think we are looking at an exceptional buildup there of ice crystal fogs, which correlates very nicely with the decrease of the prevailing temperatures at that site as measured by the spacecraft.

We've determined no particle motion. In the days when we planned Viking, we seriously debated not only the movement of dust but whether the space-craft would be disabled by the dust, We have seen no movement of dust. We talk a great deal about the southern summer season and the possibility that we may see some movement of dust at that time, but even that is in no way positive. It's just an expectation. One of the intriguing points is that we don't really know the age of the land forms we are seeing at these particular landing sites. For example, the tails of fine-grained sediment behind the boulders look like they were deposited yesterday, but they may in fact be hundreds of millions of years old.

Does the imaging investigation contribute in any way to the interpretation of the results of other experiments? I think the easiest answer is to imagine interpreting all of the Viking results — the biology results, the inorganic chemistry results, the meteorology results — without any pictures. You can see the tremendous vacuum in which we would be operating. I think right now the point is that the pictures are the matrix within which everything else is examined. Were we blindfolded, it is highly unlikely we would speak about our results in the same way.

To give you a specific example, the so called duricrust revealed by the cameras figures in the weathering arguments advanced by scientists interpreting the X-ray fluorescence results. It is often said, that the cameras make very few assumptions about what they're going to see, about how the experiment is going to run. They just look and do their thing. The liability is that because they are essentially an exploratory tool, they tend to be rather diffuse in the information they bring back to you. They don't ask a very pointed question. They don't provide data that can be fed directly into a numerical model. They speak in a much more general way. One should not expect the geomorphology within a few tens of meters to very directly reflect what's going on in the interior of the planet. That reflection would have to be very indirect.

The illusion of the letter "B" or the figure "8" on the rock at left appears to be caused by the angle of the Sun.

The famous boulder "Big Joe" pictured here is nearly seven feet long and lies about 26 feet from the spacecraft. It appears coarse-grained and is covered on the right and left by fine-grained material. Surrounding it are small sand dunes created by Martian winds.

The question "What has the imaging investigation revealed?" comes down to the issue of what you think knowledge is. What body of knowledge, somehow, is more important than another body of knowledge?

For example, consider two groups of geologists. The first group is the scientists that deal with Precambrian geology, which is the geology of Earth where you are age-dating rocks and looking. It involves looking at a segment of the Earth's history that spans several billion years. There a second group of scientists called Pleistocene geologists looks at the land forms and the rather random organization of events that have taken place over the past few millions of years, or even just thousands of years, or sometimes hundreds of years. The two groups seldom have much patience with each other because the Precambrian people think because they are dealing with a significant segment of our history, they are looking at something more fundamental. The Pleistocene people seem to be looking at events that are more random but nonetheless, they think, very important because they think they can understand them a little more clearly than more ancient events.

What you really get back to is a rather sophisticated question: "What body of knowledge do you deem, for whatever reasons, to be more important than another body of knowledge?"

What we do know from the cameras, in exquisite detail, is the descriptive detail of two sites on Mars. We know exactly what those areas look like. If you could go up there, they would look pretty much as we have seen in the pictures with some certain geometric distortions taken out. From that we can infer a possible history.

The question really comes down to: "Do you think it's important or do you think it's unimportant to have that body of knowledge?" Of course, I think it is important. But if somebody else says, "I don't think it's important," then you have to say "That of course is your privilege, and I'm sorry, but we just can't talk anymore." And if somebody says "I think it's more important to know the internal stratification of the planet, the core, the mantle, the crust," then I'll have to say "I agree. That is important, but I can't help you on that." That's where we stand.

Scientists call this rock the "Dutch Wooden Shoe" which was photographed by lander II at its landing site.

Measuring a Planet

Scientists used radio signals and radio tracking measurements from Viking to study Mars and certain aspects of the inner solar system. As they passed through space the signals were modified by the Sun, Earth, Mars and other space matter providing clues to space scientists.

Einstein's theory of general relativity predicted that a radio signal will be slowed when passing through a strong gravitational field like the Sun. The radio science team found the theory to be correct to within one-half percent and hope to test it to one-tenth of a percent.

Data extracted from the radio signals were also expected to help scientists measure the surface microwave reflectivity of Mars in the microwave range; refine the orbit and mass of Mars; estimate the planet's electronic density by measuring distortion of the Viking radio signals as they pass through the Martian atmosphere when the spacecraft swings behind the planet; measure the atmospheric turbulence by studying orbiter-lander transmissions; measure the effects of atmospheric drag; measure the electron concentration between Earth and Mars; and measure the radio signal time delay caused by the Sun during superior conjunction.

Analyses of the tracking data from the lander have yielded the accurate position coordinates for each lander, the two components of the Mars spin axis orientation to a new level of precision, and a new measurement of the Mars spin rate.

Radio Science Team: William H. Michael, Jr. (Team Leader), Langley Research Center; Joseph Brenkle, Jet Propulsion Laboratory; Dan L. Cain, Member of Technical Staff, Jet Propulsion Laboratory; John G. Davies, University of Manchester; Gunnar Fjeldbo, Systems Analysis Research Section, Jet Propulsion Laboratory; Mario D. Grossi, Consulting Scientist, Raytheon Company, Equipment Division; Irwin I. Shapiro, Professor of Geophysics and Physics, Massachusetts Institute of Technology; Leonard Tyler, Center for Radar Astronomy, Stanford University; Robert H. Tolson, NASA Langley Research Center.

Dr. William H. Michael, Jr.

The Viking radio science team is using the highly accurate radio tracking and communication systems data from the orbiters and landers to perform a number of investigations concerning the properties of Mars and its environment. Analyses of tracking data from the landers have yielded accurate position coordinates for each lander, the two components of the Mars spin axis orientation to a new level of precision, and a new measurement of the Mars spin rate.

An attempt is being made to determine spin axis precession and nutation as additional data are accumulated. These spin axis motion constants, combined with Viking gravity field data, would lead to models for mass and density distributions in the interior of Mars, with applications to its origin and history.

The two components of the spin axis orientation — right ascension and declination — had been determined prior to Viking from analysis of the motion of the two natural Martian satellites, and also from the motion of prior orbiting spacecraft. The precision was on the order of 0.2 degree in these two angular components. Now, with Viking data, the precision is at the 0.002-degree level. In other words, it has been improved by about two orders of magnitude.

Why is that important? The spin axis of Mars moves in a circular orbit over a period of about 180,000 years, called precession of the poles. The pole precesses because the gravitational field of the Sun pulls on the oblate planet Mars, with a sort of torque-coupling effect. If we can very accurately determine this spin axis motion, we would have a handle on determining the internal properties of Mars. Can we do it with the accuracy we will finally obtain from Viking data? That's still questionable, but the situation seems promising.

Our precision for the spin rate of Mars is about 2 or 3 milliseconds, or thousandths of a second, in a day. We know there is some movement of the atmosphere of Mars from the poles to the equator and back to the poles. If we could get another factor of a thousand increase in precision of the spin rate, we might be able to see a seasonal variation that could quantify the transport of mass in the atmosphere. This will be very difficult to accomplish but is worth noting.

Lander ranging data, and simultaneous dual-frequency orbiter ranging data to calibrate the effects of the solar corona, were collected during times around solar conjunction and have been used to perform the most precise time-delay test of the theory of general relativity yet achieved.

Einstein's theory of general relativity predicts that when a radio signal or light wave passes close to a strong gravitation field such as that of the Sun, the signal is slightly slowed. Specifically, the theory predicts that in the case of a light wave or radio wave coming from a spacecraft at Mars and grazing the Sun's surface, the signal would be slowed by about 240 microseconds, a relatively small amount. A preliminary look at the data confirmed that the signal slows by the expected amount to within about 0.5 percent of the prediction. In other words, the theory is right to within one-half percent and hopefully it can be tested to about one-tenth of a percent.

Why is that important? It doesn't have too much application in everyday life but is very important in fields such as gravitational theory, astrophysics, cosmology, and even in high-energy particle physics. It's very important to know the fundamental laws of physics as accurately as one can determine them. That's the goal of the test. It appears that this test is at least by a factor of four more precise than any previous tests of this effect.

Properties of the solar corona, including the electron density distribution and small-scale plasma structure, have also been determined from the near-conjunction data, which include some data closer to the Sun than any previously obtained.

Orbiter tracking data taken during occultations as the spacecraft passed behind Mars; as seen from the Earth; have been analyzed to provide information on the atmospheric properties and topography at about 50 locations on Mars at latitudes from about 80° south to 70° north. The mean atmospheric pressure at the surface agrees well with the pressure measured at the landing sites, and radii at these additional locations will provide a better determination of the figure (shape) on Mars.

Mars gravitational field properties have been obtained from analyses of the orbiter tracking data, with improved resolution of the gravity determinations in the northern hemisphere. We analyzed small changes in the spacecraft orbits to help us determine a large number of factors in an already established model of the gravitational field. With a combination of the Viking and the Mariner IX information, we have fairly good coverage from about 20° south latitude up to about 50° north latitude. We wanted to know whether the gravity field variations correlate with features seen on Mars. We have a positive correlation for the Tharsis mountains area, with relatively high gravity, and for the Hellas basin, with relatively low gravity. Geological processes or impact processes may have brought about these gravity anomalies. As the precision of the gravitational field and topography determinations increases, analyses of the near-surface mass and density distributions and related geophysical processes can be investigated.

Dramatic approach picture.

Martian Atmosphere

Dr. Michael McElroy

The upper atmosphere mass spectrometer measured the amounts of gases in the atmosphere and identified their molecules. It provided a stratified profile of the concentration of the gases in the atmosphere. The experiment was also designed to determine whether life supporting atmospheric components are present. The instruments obtained data from 143 to 62 miles above the Mars surface during descent of the lander.

The low atmosphere structure experiment gathered and combined data from lander accelerometers and aeroshell stagnation pressure and recovery temperature instruments. The combined data revealed the density, temperature and pressure profiles of the Mars atmosphere as the lander descended to the surface.

The instruments operated during the aeroshell, parachute and descent engine phases of landing. They provided information on the winds and acceleration of the lander due to Mars gravity. Temperature and pressure sensors on the lander, which were also used by the lander on the surface, recorded the temperature and pressure of the atmosphere during landing.

Also discovered was an abundance of water on Mars that is frozen or contained in the rocks. Mars has an abundance of the three important elements essential to life on Earth — water, carbon and nitrogen. Some scientists say that moving Mars closer to the Sun could melt the polar ice caps and give Mars the chance to be more like the Earth.

The complete atmospheric analysis is reported in chapter, "Search for Organics."

Entry Science Team: Alfred O.C. Nier (Team Leader), School of Physics and Astronomy, University of Minnesota; William B. Hanson, University of Texas at Dallas; Michael McElroy, Pierce Hall, Harvard University; Alvin Seiff, Staff Scientist, Office of the Center Director, Ames Research Center; and Nelson Spencer, Chief, Laboratory for Planetary Atmospheres, Goddard Space Flight Center.

Mars is being very cooperative and has given us some bonus information we really didn't expect. We have defined what the Martian atmosphere is made of with a precision almost as good as we know the composition of the Earth's atmosphere, and that's a major step forward. But we expected to find the chemical composition. We did not expect to get clues as to the evolution of the planet from its isotopic abundance.

For example, we found that Mars has more of the heavy form of nitrogen than Earth does. That allows us to say a lot about the history of Mars. Mars is remarkably Earth-like although it has gone through a different evolutionary history. A lot of the past information about the Earth is lost to our scientists. They can't recover it because the Earth is exceedingly dynamic. The great hope is that by combining information we have from Mars with information from Earth we will learn much more about both places. Mars is not just an exciting place in its own right. We cannot hope to understand the Earth without having the advantage of the data Mars can provide us. Mars has a lot of the clues about the early stages of the solar system.

There are two abundant isotopes of nitrogen. One, Mass 14, which is the common form, the other, Mass 15, which is less common. They are both present in the Earth's atmosphere and they are both also present in Martian atmosphere. Mars has rather more of the heavy component than the Earth has. The implication is that Mars must have lost the light material over the age of the planet. Knowing how much is now there, you can also make a statement about how much was there in the beginning. And that lets you make a rather direct statement about the history of Mars as far as the nitrogen is concerned. Particularly it makes it obvious that Mars had quite a lot of nitrogen to begin with and has lost quite a lot over geologic time. The initial amount of nitrogen on Mars appears not to be terribly different from the initial amount of nitrogen on Earth. The slightly lower gravity on Mars allows nitrogen to escape. On Earth, nitrogen does not escape at all. Mars has simply

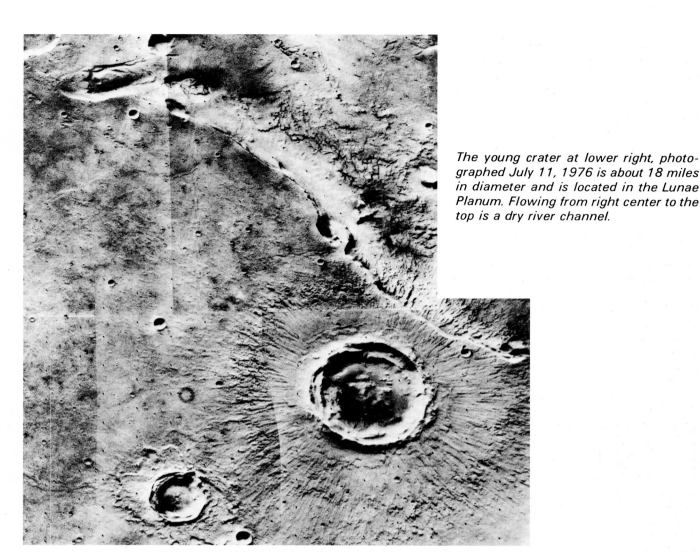

The young crater at lower right, photographed July 11, 1976 is about 18 miles in diameter and is located in the Lunae Planum. Flowing from right center to the top is a dry river channel.

evolved to a larger extent than the Earth because of this escape process.

The most abundant volatile material on Earth is water. The second most abundant is carbon, present mostly as carbon dioxide. The third most abundant is nitrogen. All of these elements are obviously present on Mars in fairly appreciable amounts.

The indication that the permanent polar cap is made of pure water ice shows that Mars has lots of water. Observation of atmospheric water vapor on Mars shows that the rocks themselves contain lots of water. Mars may in fact have more water then the Earth has.

Mars has lots of carbon dioxide which makes up 95 percent of its atmosphere. That is as much as it can hold at the present temperature. Our theory on the escape of nitrogen says that Mars started out with a lot of nitrogen perhaps comparable amounts to the Earth.

As far as the three most abundant volatiles are concerned, Mars has a lot of each of them, just as the Earth does.

Next we look at the measurement of the noble gases — argon, krypton and xenon. The curious thing is that Mars, in terms of the relative abundance of those gases, is also Earth-like.

The overall statement is that as far as the volatiles are concerned, the two planets are very similar. It looks as though they had a common origin, from the same kind of material in the solar nebula, but have gone through a slightly different history.

The difference is, first of all, that Mars is a little bit smaller and has less gravity. Second, Mars is colder and so retains more water in frozen form and contains more carbon dioxide in ice form.

I think if you were to take the Earth and move it out away from the Sun, generating an ice age, Earth's oceans would freeze over and go into ice form. Once you did that, there would be a tendency for carbon dioxide to pile up in the atmosphere of the Earth. By moving Earth far enough away from the Sun, you could make it very Mars-like, or correspondingly, if you take the view that Mars is currently undergoing an ice age, once it comes out of that ice age it looks like a much more hospitable place. The chemical ingredients necessary to make it a more hospitable place are present on Mars. It's just a question of whether the temperature is high enough to allow the material to get out of the rocks.

When life became profuse on the Earth, which happened at least two billion years ago, the entire characteristics of the atmosphere changed. Earth's atmosphere started to evolve a lot of oxygen. In the process, a lot of mineral transformations occurred. Rocks tended to move from reduced mineral assemblages to fairly oxidized states so the early chemistry of the Earth's crust and its atmosphere has all disappeared. It's all been worked over by chemical processes directly related to the presence of life and the profuse nature of life on Earth. Mars, on the other hand, has obviously preserved a lot of that early history to a better extent.

By working the problem of both planets, you can hope to really explain the initial conditions for Earth. I think the great challenge is that if you can make a sensible statement about the probable composition of early Earth, can you then predict how it would evolve forward in time and can you get to the point where it is inevitable that life should evolve? Is a complex organic chemistry a necessary condition for the Earth or is it some kind of peculiar accident?

I think we got much more out of Viking than we really anticipated. The exciting thing is to really look at a new world in a fairly complete way for the first time. The clues that emerge don't just come from one instrument, they come from the whole assembly of experiments. It's the interplay, which was not entirely predictable, but that happened and forced many of us to do things which we did not anticipate doing. For example, right now I'm being forced to try to really understand meteorites a lot more than I ever realized I would have to because it's clear they can also provide more information to this whole puzzle.

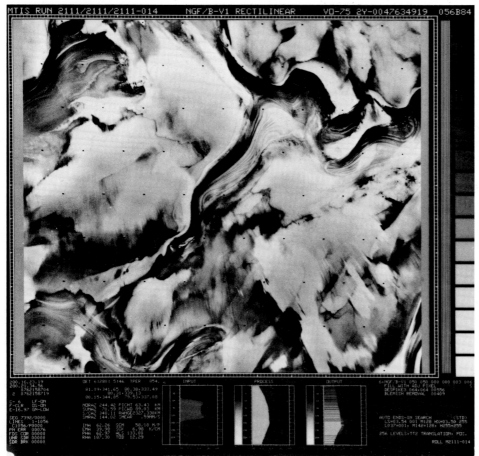

This photograph of the Martian polar cap shows the scarp thought to be an erosional feature. The variety of arc-shaped cliffs illustrates the complexity of erosion in the northern polar region. The dune-like features and darker areas with rippled texture are common. The material that forms the dunes is thought to come from eroded layered terrain. The ice, of unknown thickness, was once thought to be carbon dioxide ice, but has now proved to be water ice.

On the Desert

The physical properties experiment was actually a composite of information collected from virtually all the lander experiments. By studying all aspects of the lander operation, from landing through conduct of each experiment, enough data were collected to define the physical properties of the Martian soil.

Although the moisture on Mars was found to be as sparse as the deserts of the southwest United States, the surface material behaves as if it were wet sand. No amount of moisture on Earth would produce prolonged cohesion as high as the dry soil on Mars. Scientists believe the cohesion to be basically electrical.

The density of the surface material on Mars is nearly identical to that on the Earth, meaning the density of the rocks and particle sizes are the same on both planets. Gravity was found to be one-third as strong on Mars as it is on the Earth.

The instruments, housed in the lander, provided good estimates of the bulk density of the surface material showing the density higher in the rocky flats area than in the sandy flats area, a difference also found on the Earth.

Physical Properties Team: Richard W. Shorthill (Team Leader), Geospace Sciences Lab, University of Utah Research Institute; Robert E. Hutton, Senior Staff Engineer, Advanced Technology Staff, TRW Systems Group; Henry Moore II, Department of the Interior, U.S. Geological Survey; and Ronald Scott, Department of Engineering & Applied Science, Thomas Laboratory, California Institute of Technology.

Dr. Richard W. Shorthill

The physical properties experiment was successful in meeting its goal of characterizing the soils or surface material of Mars. What we found is not what one would normally think of when one talks about soils on Earth.

We were able to get an estimate of bulk density, that is the number of grams per cubic centimeter, at the two landing sites. At Viking I for example, we found that the bulk density in the so-called rocky flats area was a little higher than it was in the sandy flats area. At the second landing site, we found that the bulk density was higher than the sandy flats area. We actually were able to obtain soil properties by looking at the sides of the trenches and the trenches in general. The particle size and the particle size distribution is harder to determine. We put together a lot of measurements and pictures and we still haven't tied that down completely.

One of the things we did that we hadn't thought of trying before the landing was to measure the penetration resistance. We first thought that we would push the surface sampler into the soil until the motor "clutched," but there was a lot of resistance by the directors of the project not to do that because we had buckled the boom before in testing. However, during the mission we just pushed the back hoe into the surface activating a microswitch (we knew exactly what the force was that activated the switch) and were able to determine the penetration resistance. We got a picture of the back hoe each time.

Cohesion and adhesion are interesting things to measure. The cohesion (how the particles stick to each other) was determined from the dimensions of the trench and the heights of the side walls. It is related to the collapse of the walls. The adhesion was probably a little more difficult to determine. We did this by looking at the soil that stuck to the sides of the surface sampler head before and after it vibrated. We actually did some laboratory accelerometer tests on the vibrator at Martin Marietta while we were still on the surface of Mars to get a calibration of the adhesive forces.

As far as the temperatures we measured, the footpad temperature is still a little bit of a mystery because we haven't been able to photograph the thermocouples on Viking I. However, the pictures so far show they may be partially covered which is consistent with the temperature curves we see. On Viking II we think that the footpad temperature sensor is not buried, which is consistent with what we see. Unfortunately, the orientation of the lander and the latitude produce shadows that pass over the thermosensor so the temperature curve is not a nice, smooth curve. It first rises to a relative peak and then levels, it rises again and is flat, then it rises a little more after noon and follows a predicted pattern. But if we understand the shadow prediction model, we understand what's happening. The actual swing in temperature is smaller than expected.

The only thing we haven't been able to get a handle on yet is the ultraviolet flux at the surface using passive ultraviolet paints that darken with exposure to ultraviolet. From the two ultraviolet chips we're photographing, we hope to get a feeling or an indication of what the ultraviolet flux is at the surface, but they seem to not darken as fast as we had expected. We will have to do more calibration tests at Langley. Fortunately, we have some chips that were made from the same paint-batch mixture.

The moisture content of the Martian soil is low. If you wanted something as dry on Earth, you would have to go to one of our southwest deserts. It may however, be difficult to produce a trench like we see on Mars. Only on a beach where the sand is a little wet would you be able to dig a trench that looks like the one we made on Mars. On Earth, you have to put moisture in to get the cohesion high enough to make a trench similar to what we see in the dry soil of Mars.

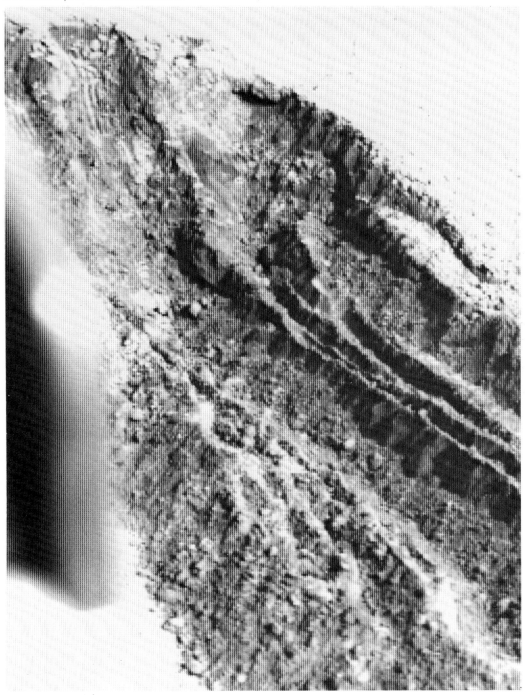

In an attempt to reach soil a foot beneath the surface, lander I dug this six inch deep, 12 inch wide, 29 inch long trench, February 12 and 14, 1977. It was dug by repeated backhoeing in a left-right center pattern. The clods of soil and the steepness of the trench walls indicate the material is cohesive and behaves something like ordinary flour.

The Red Planet

The magnetic properties experiment revealed an abundance of magnetic particles on the Martian surface. This high abundance was found both in the soil and in the very fine dust. On Earth the most common magnetic particles are either iron metal as in the moon or in meteorites or iron oxides. The experiment indicated the red coloration of Mars is caused by a highly oxidized iron that is normally non-magnetic on Earth.

Magnetic Properties Team: Robert B. Hargraves (Team Leader), Department of Geological and Geophysical Sciences, Guyot Hall, Princeton University.

Dr. Robert B. Hargraves

The most outstanding result of our experiment has been the evident high abundance of magnetic particles both in the soil and in the very fine dust. This was quite a surprise. On Earth, and probably anywhere in the solar system. the most common magnetic particles are either iron metal, as in the moon or in meteorites, or iron oxides. With a planet as red as Mars, we don't think it's likely to be iron metal. What one would most expect by terrestrial analogy would be iron oxide, of which there are two on Earth — magnetite (or lodestone Fe_3O_4), which is black or grey, and an unusual form of gamma Fe_2O_4 called maghemite that is surprisingly magnetic. However, the red coloration suggests highly oxidized iron of which the common form on Earth is called hematite alpha (Fe_2O_3) and it is essentially nonmagnetic. This cannot be the candidate material we have up there. Although maghemite is Fe_2O_4, it has the magnetic properties of magnetite (Fe_3O_4). We know that maghemite occurs on Earth in certain environments, as in Hawaii. It is usually thought to be the product of low-temperature oxidation of preexisting magnetite. You oxidize it but you inherit the structure and magnetic properties of the preexisting magnetite.

By terrestrial analogy, if you had to say what the magnetic mineral on Mars is most likely to be; magnetite or maghemite, I think the majority of people would think of magnetite. But Mars is a different planet. From what we've seen from the Martian imagery, these magnetic particles themselves appear red and they appear virtually indistinguishable from the average surface material on Mars. Magnetite normally is blackish-gray. Either it's magnetite, with a coating of red hematite and that would mean the particle was composite, or it could be just a particle of γFe_2O_3, which is reddish-brown and is in its own right magnetic.

If it is the magnetite, the implication is that the extent of interaction between the surface particles and the atmosphere has not been very great. If there were intensive interaction and weathering in the conventional terrestrial style, one would expect all the magnetite to be oxidized to hematite, which is nonmagnetic. But, on Mars it could be oxidized to γFe_2O_3, which behaves like magnetite. In other words, it is completely oxidized but the ferric oxide is magnetic. But we cannot say which it is on the basis of the magnetic properties.

We are stuck at the moment with this dilemma and I see no way to resolve it. The main point is that there is a lot of magnetic material up there and either of the two explanations is intriguing. We are not going to have data that will directly resolve it. At the moment, the most we can hope for is to marshal lots of supporting data that may make a rather impressive argument in favor of the conclusion that the magnetic mineral is mostly maghemite.

The lander I collector head of the surface sampler is full of Martian soil destined for the organic chemistry experiment August 3, 1976.

In Search of a Pebble

The inorganic chemistry investigation was designed to analyze the chemical elements in the Martian soil. The instrument used was an X-ray fluorescence spectrometer that can analyze most elements known to exist in the solar system.

Lander I completed five successful sample acquisitions, three collected during the primary mission and two during the extended mission. The acquisitions for lander II total four, one collected during the primary mission and three during the extended mission. They collected 620 cubic centimeters of Martian soil. Each sample has been sifted through a funnel to get the correct size and then charged with high velocity particles or photons from an X-ray source.

When the X-ray fluorescence spectrometer was supplied with a sample of the surface material, the first return of data was sufficient to detect the presence of the elements iron, calcium, silicon, titanium and aluminum as major constituents.

Lander II attempted to retrieve rock samples three times and failed. What had appeared to be rocks in lander pictures turned out to be small crustal particles that crumbled when picked up by the surface sampler. The scientists believe there are pebbles available, but they have been unable to analyze one.

The following table shows the final results of the experiment. The figures cover the entire range of analyses and samples taken during the primary mission at the two lander sites.

Maximum limits, %	Element
0 to 8	Magnesium
1.5 to 7	Aluminum
15 to 30	Silicon
2 to 7	Sulphur
0 to 2	Cesium
0 to 2.5	Potassium
2 to 6	Calcium
0.1 to 1	Titanium
12 to 16	Iron

Inorganic Chemistry Team: Priestley Toulmin III (Team Leader), U.S. Geological Survey; Alex K. Baird, Department of Geology, Pomona College; Benton C. Clark, Martin Marietta Aerospace; Klaus Keil, Professor of Geology and Director, Institute of Meteoritics, University of New Mexico; Harry J. Rose, Jr., U.S. Geological Survey.

Dr. Benton C. Clark

The most striking factor between the two Viking landing sites is that the soil composition is extremely similar in both cases. This is true for all elements we can detect in the soil, including the very high sulphur content observed at lander I and also found at lander II. This would be a very strange thing to happen on Earth because the two landers are four thousand miles apart. Even on the Moon, at that distance you would not find the composition that similar in general.

The general explanation for why this happens on Mars is that the giant dust storms that occur approximately every two years apparently mix up the soil very efficiently and distribute it all over the planet as a fairly uniform mixture.

Just because at two points it measures the same is not proof that the entire planet is covered with exactly the same material. However, the lander imaging team has recently come to the conclusion that the fine soil surrounding both landers is the same color and has the same spectral response. This is the light spectra, including infrared, that are called the bright areas on Mars as seen through telescopes from Earth. These bright areas cover the majority of the planet. There are some dark areas that may be mostly where dead rock or a large quantity of solid rock is showing.

The interesting thing is that, even with this generalization, we find when you sample different areas at the same lander site you can get differences in soil chemistry. In one case, we get a higher sulphur content when we pick up a little dirt clod. In other cases, when we push rock aside and sample the surface directly beneath the rock, we in general get a lower iron content and a somewhat higher sulphur content. This leads one to the idea that the soil under rocks may be material that has been lying there a longer period of time and may be an older soil, whereas material out in the free area may be a result of more recent dust storms — recent in this case meaning the last thousands to millions of years.

We spent a lot of time searching for pebbles because the chemistry of the soil does not match that of any rock. We at first thought that we might obtain a fine material by simply grinding up some particular kind of known rock such as a basalt. Since it is different, the question then is, is it because the rocks have been weathered very extensively and had their components separated out into different groups and is the soil just one particular grouping of the material that has been weathered out?

If we could acquire a rock and measure its chemistry and then compare it with the soil we would be able to tell in what manner the soil was produced. For example, was a lot of liquid water involved? The other thing we could tell if we could find good original rocks, particularly volcanic type rocks, was what the bedrock is like and the deeper lined rock. Perhaps it could even reflect the composition of what we would call the mantle of Mars. This would tell us how the planet has evolved over the history of its formation, how the various rock materials have formed, and to what extent some of their chemical constituents such as iron may have sunk into a core.

We were able to determine the contents of pebbles only by inference. We believe that the soil could only have been derived from rocks of the so-called mafic or ultramafic group. These are rocks with a very high magnesium and iron content.

Regarding sulphur, it is almost a hundred times higher than you would find in the Earth's soil or in lunar soil. It could mean a couple of things. It might mean that Mars is just very rich in sulphur to begin with. Or it might mean that Mars is more like the composition of the Earth or the Moon, except the soil has been exposed to a fairly large action of water. In this case the water would be dissolving the sulphur throughout a large thickness. As the water evaporates, it moves up toward the surface where it evaporates and brings with it whatever is soluble. The sulphur, we think, is in the form of magnesium sulphate, which is more commonly known as epsum salts. We know that this is extremely soluble material. It's about as soluble as table salt, or sodium chloride, in water. As the water evaporates it would move this material up toward the surface and since we're only sampling the surface that's what we may be finding. You must remember that we're looking at samples of only about 30 cc, or about 3, 4, or 5 tablespoons — about a half cup.

The idea of weathered material versus fresh rocks is that the soil is not the same composition as one would expect by simply grinding up one of the kinds of rocks such as the basalt. The way this happens on Earth (you also find that Earth soil does not match any type of rock in general) is mainly because of the action of water, but also to some extent oxygen. Water more or less dissolves the rock and things that are easily dissolved are going to form the soil. Things that are hard to dissolve — the residual material — ends up located somewhere else. This separates things out and produces in this case two soils with different composition. If you averaged them together, they

Two views of trenches dug by lander I in the Martian soil show that as dry as the soil is, it clings together much like wet sand. Samples have shown the soil to have a high iron content and to be very complex because of the magnetic particles found in it. Bromine and Chlorine have also been found, making the Martian soil more Earth-like than Lunar-like. The shadow above is the meterology boom.

Weathering of the rock strewn surface of Mars at lander I shows sand drifted from left to right.

would come back to the rock composition again. So the fact that the Martian soil is not like the rock makes us believe that something like this happened on Mars and the only way we know this can happen readily is to get water involved pretty heavily.

It's the old question "Was it a whole lot of water for a short period of time, or a little bit of water for millions or billions of years?" It could be either situation and it's hard for us to say.

Probably the most interesting general thing we have learned on this experiment is that the soil on Mars is different from any soil on Earth or the Moon or in any meteorite.

The second aspect is that the soil has very high iron, which we suspected because Mars is so reddish. But it also has very high sulphur, which is surprising. We have a soil that is different and has very high components of some things. We know that the Martian soil is extremely complex because it has magnetic particles in it. It has the high iron and high sulphur. It has chlorine so evidently it has a very high salt content. By the way, we have very recently come to the conclusion that the soil also contains bromine. That goes along with the chlorine. If you have some very high chlorine salts, you usually have some bromine, but you very seldom have as much as we've seen. This makes the Martian soil very different from

lunar soil and more Earth-like in some respects. Lunar soil is much more primitive.

The complex nature of Martian soil indicates that Mars has had a very significant history that includes the action of liquid water. The distance to the Sun does come into play, and the $64,000 question is "Did Mars just start out with less of the volatile elements such as water?" We have tried to go back far enough to determine why Earth has more water. There are various theories. In fact the theory that has been most popular up to now is that Mars should have more water. That theory comes from the fact that the further you are away from the Sun, the more of these volatile elements you have. The outer planets in fact have extremely volatile elements like hydrogen and helium. The predictions were that Mars should have more than the Earth and the Earth should have more than Venus, and so forth. But it just doesn't seem to be turning out to be the case. One of the other ideas that just recently has been put forth is that Mars is small compared to the Earth and maybe you get more of these volatiles if you are larger.

Marsquakes

The seismic investigations were to provide data on volcanic activity, planet structural shift and meteorite impacts on the planet's surface. The instrument would detect seismic activity through a pendulum and a signal coil mounted on flexible pivots and suspended between two magnets on top of the lander. Ground movement causes the pendulum to move, displacing the coil and causing a small current proportional to the displacement.

By comparing the variations in the data generated by the instruments on both landers, the nature of the planet's structure and the source of seismic activity could be determined. However, on lander I it is clear that the seismometer gyroscope did not uncage in any axis and the instrument is inoperable. The seismometer on lander II performed nominally at all times.

The detection of a magnitude 3 Marsquake was compared to an Earthquake allowing scientists to estimate the mean crustal thickness in the Viking II landing site. It turned out to be half the crustal thickness of the continental parts of Earth and 50 percent greater than the average thickness of the oceanic crust. Viking II landed in the area of Mars where the crust is the thinnest.

Seismology Team: Don L. Anderson (Team Leader), Seismological Laboratory, California Institute of Technology; Robert Kovach, Professor of Geophysics, Department of Geophysics, Stanford University; Gary V. Latham, Division of Earth and Planetary Sciences, Marine Biomedical Institute, University of Texas Medical Branch; Dr. George Sutton, University of Hawaii at Manoa, Hawaii Institute of Geophysics; and M. Nafi Toksoz, Professor of Geophysics, Department of Earth and Planetary Sciences, Massachusetts Institute of Technology.

Dr. Don L. Anderson

We have learned that we can operate a very sensitive seismometer on the surface of Mars. We were afraid we wouldn't be able to do this because of the high winds on Mars that could affect a sensitive instrument. It turns out that during the night, from about 6 p.m. through the next morning, the winds die down to about virtually zero and the seismic background noises are essentially zero. During this time we can operate a seismometer at a very high sensitivity.

At the moment we can record Marsquakes as small as a magnitude of 3 at a distance at about 125 miles and since we've been operating we have detected one such event. It turns out that this quake was about a magnitude of 3 at about a distance of 75 miles or so. It looks almost exactly like an Earthquake in southern California I recorded on an identical instrument at California Institute of Technology. By comparing the two events, the Marsquake and the Earthquake, we were able to estimate the mean crustal thickness at the Viking II landing site. It turns out to be about 9 to 11 miles — about half the thickness of the crust in the continental parts of the Earth and about 50 percent greater than the average thickness of the oceanic crust.

This immediately allows us to infer crustal thickness all over the planet. In particular, the crust can get as thick as approximately 50 miles. This is much thicker than the crust under the continental regions of the Earth. The crust in the Viking II landing site is probably as thin or thinner than any other place on the planet except the Helous Basin, which has a very thin crust and might in fact have zero crust.

Another unexpected result of the seismic experiment is a vast amount of information about the winds on Mars. The seismometer is a very sensitive wind detector. It picks up the wind pressure on the lander and we can determine the characteristics of the wind to complement the direct measurements of the wind made by the meteorological experiments.

In particular, we discovered this pattern of the winds dying down about 6 p.m. But this changed very rapidly on the 131st Martian day. The winds on that day started to blow all night until 2 or 3 a.m. indicating, a substantial change in the weather patterns. If very high winter winds had continued at night, they could have generated the massive dust storms we have observed in the winter time. However, as of November 1977, orbiter photographs have shown only a few isolated dust storms but none reaching the magnitude of the planetwide dust storm of 1971.

We had no idea whether Mars would be more or less seismologically active than the Earth. We suspected that it would be less active. Most Earthquakes are associated with the plates moving around. We knew that probably wasn't happening on Mars. On the other hand, there are many little Moonquakes and many Earthquakes in what are considered non-tectonic regions of the Earth such as midcontinental regions. We suspected we would indeed measure Marsquakes but we had no idea how many there would be or how large they would be. We can't say that any discovery would be surprising. The other part of the seismological investigation is to determine the structure of the interior of the planet such as its crustal thickness. Here again, we had no particular basis for believing whether the crust was thick or thin before we went there. That's what the experiment was all about.

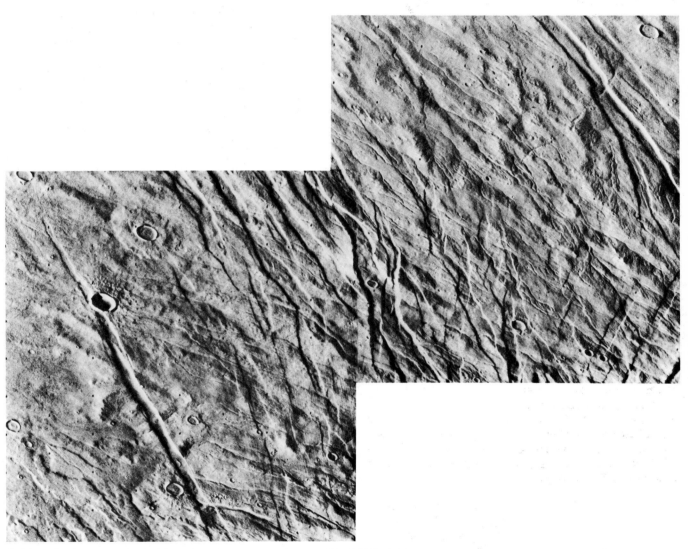

Orbiter II photographed this volcanic plateau August 15, 1976, in the northern lowlands. The crust is broken by many faults. Small channels are offset by the faults, showing they are older than the faults. Craters made by impacting meteorites indicate some older and some younger than the faults. The photo was taken from a distance of 2500 miles.

Lander Performance

The Viking lander completed two basic mission roles: (1) landing safely at a preselected landing site on the Mars surface, and (2) providing a favorable environment for the instruments to carry out their investigations during entry and on the surface.

Guidance Control and Sequencing Computer

As the lander began its solo journey to Mars, the guidance control and sequencing computer controlled and commanded all the operations. It also performed the navigation, guidance and steering functions necessary for separation from the orbiter and the landing sequence. The guidance and control computer spent most of its time from prelaunch to landing preparing and checking the landing systems to be sure they would carry out their duties. On the basis of the success of these tests, the computer commanded separation from the orbiter and sent signals to begin the landing sequence.

Deorbit Engines

The first major event was deorbit burn by the eight engines on the lander's aeroshell. The burn time for lander I was 1759.8 seconds and for lander II was 1757.1 seconds. Landers I and II were off in their projected burn times by only 2.8 and 0.1 seconds, respectively. While still within limits, the attitude rates, or the specific orientation of the landers, did exceed predictions.

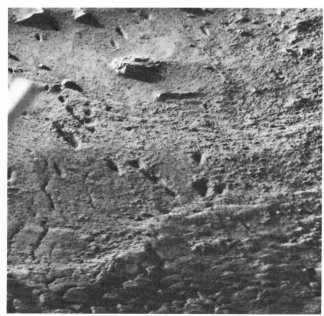

Indentations of the soft Martian soil in the center of this photo are thought to be caused by rocks thrown out upon lander II's impact on the Martian surface.

Lander I's meterology boom contains instruments to measure atmospheric pressure, temperature, wind velocity and direction.

Computer

Based on a preprogrammed time from deorbit burn and before predicted entry, the capsules were oriented for entry and to collect high-altitude science data. These maneuvers were performed exactly as planned. Should something have gone wrong, the computer had the capability to operate the lander without commands from Earth. All deorbit and landing commands were stored in the computer since signals took 20 minutes to travel from Earth to Mars at the time of landing.

Radar Altimeter

Entry into the Martian atmosphere had been arbitrarily defined as 800,000 feet, although the atmosphere is apparent at 300,000 feet. The altitude estimates used in the navigation computer program were markedly improved because the radar altimeters were turned on at entry and worked nearly

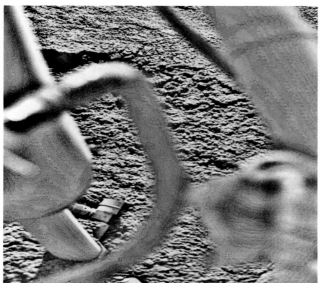

Lander I footpad, #3 at lower left, sank five inches into the fine-grained soil. At right is the high-gain antenna on lander I.

perfectly on both landers. The initial error caused by the difference between inertial altitude estimates and radar altitude measurements was 11,000 feet for lander I and 300 feet for lander II. Convergence time is the period required to reduce the difference in the two figures to about 2 percent of the initial error. The data were first used in navigation at about 258,600 feet.

Aeroshell

The aerodynamic portion of the entry phase was perfect. The landers stayed within the designed limits. During the entry phase the aeroshell became a focal point. This inner capsule consisted of a heatshield, which faced the direction of Mars, and a base cover which contained the parachute system. A half-inch layer of cork-like material bonded to the outside of the aeroshell protected the lander from aerodynamic heating during entry. The ablative material burned away carrying heat with it. Although the heating sensor on the lander I base cover failed, no detrimental effects were observed. The sensor on lander II showed a reading slightly higher than the designed limits.

The thermal subsystems performed nominally from separation through landing. All component temperatures were within flight acceptance test limits and structural temperatures were well within design limits. At touchdown, internal temperatures were generally 4 to 8° cooler than predicted. Because the lander interior is an insulated compartment, its temperature is primarily the result of component power consumption, and only slightly affected by

external environmental factors during the landing sequence. The total power consumption was below expectations, which was consistent with the lower temperature experienced.

The landers experienced peak deceleration somewhere between 79,000 and 98,000 feet above the surface of Mars. For awhile, the path leveled off into horizontal flight because of the aerodynamic lift provided by the aeroshell. Continued deceleration caused the landers to resume descent.

The Bioshield

The aeroshell and the lander were protected from biological, chemical and particulate contamination before and during launch by the bioshield. The two-piece dome-shaped outer capsule was sealed around the lander and the aeroshell with silicone rubber. After launch, the seal was broken and the bioshield cap jettisoned. The umbrella-shaped base traveled on to Mars with the spacecraft to protect the lander from any contaminants that may have been on the orbiter. Scientists feared the lander might be contaminated during interplanetary flight.

The base was released from the orbiter after the lander was separated for its landing on Mars. The bioshield base separation was essential as it restricted the field of view of the orbiter scan platform. The base separation went according to plan on orbiter I, however orbiter II had some problems. The explosive devices used to spring the base latches caused a shock that jolted orbiter II out of proper attitude. Communication was lost for a matter of minutes, but more seriously one of the command processors was lost. More explosions would have been necessary to spring the base and the Viking scientists thought the one remaining command processor too valuable to risk. The orbiter II base was not separated until early 1978 after much of the mission was complete. The separation was accomplished without damage to the orbiter.

Parachute

After the aeroshell had slowed the lander from approximately 10,294 miles per hour to 670 miles per hour, the 53-foot parachute was deployed at an altitude of 19,300 feet. The parachute was jettisoned at approximately 4000 feet after slowing the lander to

Orbiter I's nuclear power system, the U.S. flag and a Bicentennial symbol.

138 miles per hour. The parachute was fired from a canister at 90 feet per second. Very little wind was encountered during the parachute maneuver. The aeroshell was released pyrotechnically 7 seconds after parachute deployment. During that time, the radar altimeter was temporarily inhibited to allow transfer of the signal from the aeroshell antenna to a lander antenna. From that point on, the radar altimeter and the velocity radar were working together. The error between the estimates and measurements were quickly converged in less than 3 seconds as required for terminal descent.

Terminal Descent and Landing Radar

On both landers the terminal descent and landing radar (TDLR) channel 2 detected the presence of the aeroshell as it fell away. The radar had four beams

that lock onto the ground for sensing the position of the lander relative to the surface of Mars. According to plan, a drop lock, or termination of the beam readings on the surface, took place momentarily to prevent the radar from confusing the falling aeroshell with the Martian surface. The drop lock lasted for 1 minute and, reacquiring lock, the planet's surface was sensed.

Pyrotechnics

All 29 pyrotechnic events occurred in proper sequence to perform the series of jettison maneuvers aboard the lander.

Landing Engines

The final landing phase began with engine ignition while the landers were still attached to the parachutes. This maneuver started at an altitude of 4800 feet. Following a 2-second engine warmup period, the parachute and base cover were separated. The three throttleable landing engines, mounted at 120-degree intervals on the lander body, slowed the spacecraft to about 5.5 miles per hour by the time it reached the Mars surface. Each engine is throttleable between 62 and 638 pounds of thrust to control descent. Throttling commands come from the guidance control and sequencing computer based on data from the landing computers.

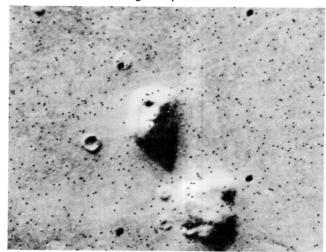

A rock formation (center) and the image of a human head formed by shadows. The feature is one mile across.

The maneuvers were performed so the spacecraft could land essentially vertical. Both landers entered the final descent phase 8 feet higher than expected, resulting in the landing phase taking 1 second longer. The delay was caused by an accumulation of negligible errors in the different landing systems. Just prior to the final descent phase, the spacecraft had been slowed to a speed of 8.2 feet per second. Attitude perturbations and rates were almost zero during the entire terminal descent phase. The landing legs were deployed and a roll maneuver completed to give the spacecraft proper orientation.

Touchdown was nearly perfect. A minor incident with the engines occurred when both landers indicated a momentary increase in throttle settings for one or more engines. This has been attributed to the radar sensing dust blown up from the planet in the last few feet of descent.

Landing Legs and Footpads

The lander's legs were in a stowed postion while the lander was tucked inside the aeroshell. When the aeroshell separated, the legs were extended into position for landing. After absorbing the final impact on the planet, the legs immediately sent a signal through the guidance control and sequencing computer to shut down the landing engines. The lander I data indicate leg 2 probably touched the surface first followed by legs 1 and 3. At a landing velocity of 8.2 feet per second, a stroke of approximately 3 inches was experienced by legs 1 and 3, which took more of the initial shock than leg 2, which buried itself in the Martian dust about 8 inches. Leg 3 probably touched first, and because of a slightly smaller stroke than leg 1, a sizeable rock may be partially supporting the lander somewhere under the body or propellant tank near leg 3. Whatever the cause, no damage has been observed.

Communications

After landing, the computer turned off such descent and landing systems as the entry science instruments and the landing instruments. Next the direct-to-Earth antenna was oriented and commanded the transmitters to send stored data either to Earth or to the orbiter. This initial lander relay link lasted 15 minutes without incident.

The lander communications subsystem consisted of an ultrahigh frequency (UHF) relay link between the lander and the orbiter and a direct S-band link between the lander and Earth. The UHF uses three commandable output power levels. The level selected depends on the complexity of the data to be transmitted. Accurate reception of high data rates requires a high transmitter power level. Complex data such as lander pictures require high data rates. The lander S-band link provided for transmission of high-volume scientific, photographic and telemetry data directly to Earth, and received commands from Earth.

The first transmission from the lander was the UHF link to the orbiter with real-time feedthrough of data to Earth via the orbiter S-band telemetry.

The lander RSL (receiver signal level) was the sole indicator of lander II's progress toward the Martian surface when the real-time feedthrough capability was interrupted after separation. The data were recorded for later playback. The communication showed no evidence of a lander II malfunction throughout the critical entry.

On both landers, eleven seconds after landing, the data rate was switched to 16 bits per second. This event was monitored through the orbiter UHF telemetry receiver and provided the only real-time verification that lander II had successfully reached the Martian surface. The relay radio equipment on landers I and II performed exactly as expected throughout the separation-to-landing mission phase.

A portion of the initial data from lander I indicated a problem. The downlink data showed that the low gain antenna command receiver was not coherently locked with the uplink, meaning it had not reached a mutually identified frequency for transmission. It apparently drifted into lock after scanning the frequencies to determine the proper frequency for the uplink lock several minutes before the first commands were received. The problem existed in one low-gain antenna receiver when it failed to acquire the uplink signal on the second day on Mars. To bypass the problem, all commands were processed through the high gain antenna receiver. Further tests revealed the failure in the receiver was related to temperature.

The telemetry data sequence from separation through touchdown was designed to preclude loss of data if the lander-to-orbiter link was interrupted. This was accomplished by transmitting all the data twice, first in real time, and again one minute later. Interruptions in the link were considered possible for the period just after separation because of the strong lander signal and the short distance to the orbiter relay receiver. The predictions for interruptions appear to have been conservative since no interruptions were observed on either lander.

Data Storage Memory

Once landed, the UHF radios could only transmit from the lander to the orbiter for 20 minutes each day when the orbiter is within about 3000 miles of the landing site. The S-band radios could only transmit data to Earth about two hours each day, leaving long periods when the lander is collecting data and cannot transmit.

The data memory stored the scientific information gathered by the lander instruments until it could be transmitted. It also retained the entry science data collected during the communication blackout caused by ionization of the spacecraft's protective heatshield into a halo of charged particles surrounding the spacecraft. The instrument performed according to specifications on both landers.

Data Acquisition and Processing Unit

The engineering and scientific information from the lander instruments and components were collected by the data acquisition and processing unit. It worked as an informational traffic cop feeding information into the main data stream where it was transmitted directly to Earth or stored in the memory or the tape recorder. It made sure there were no overloads in the data storage memory and the tape recorder. It also directed the flow of commands throughout the electronic system. The unit has performed perfectly on both landers with no loss of commands or information.

Tape Recorder

About 20 minutes before the touchdown, the lander tape recorder turned on and recorded all transmitted data through touchdown. Had the lander-to-orbiter relay link failed or been badly degraded during this entry and descent phase, the data would have been recovered by tape recorder. The telemetry subsystem executed its planned operations for both landers during the phase without incident. Lander II separation was not received in real time because of the orbiter orientation problem, but the tape recorder was able to play back the information a few hours later.

Inertial Reference Unit

The inertial reference unit had two primary purposes — to supply attitude and velocity change information to the guidance control and sequencing computer during landing; and, to supply acceleration data to the data acquisition and processing unit for use by the entry science team. It essentially served as the inner ear to the larger brain — the guidance control computer.

After landing the unit supplied the digital data containing the lander's position on the planet used by the guidance control and sequencing computer to orient the high-gain S-band antenna toward Earth. Approximately 6 minutes after landing the inertial reference unit was switched off and no longer used. No problems were encountered on either lander.

Power

The power subsystem supported the landers as anticipated from separation to their successful touchdown on Mars. The power systems on the landers performed incredibly close to the nominal mission load profiles. Four batteries inside the lander body supplied power to the lander science instruments and other systems during periods of high activity. After touchdown, the lander batteries were recharged in a surprisingly short time, indicating the energy used during descent was 100 watt-hours less than predicted for lander I and 50 watt-hours less for lander II.

Surface Sampler

Three minor problems with the surface samplers on both landers did not interfere with conduct of the experiments. First, a latch pin failed to drop from the surface sampler boom on lander I because of insufficient extension of the boom during the initial sequence. When the boom was retracted, the latch pin prevented it from completing the sequence. Teams of engineers simulated the problems of Earth to determine a solution. The boom was extended beyond the initial position, causing the pin to drop out.

The second difficulty was experienced when the boom failed to retract after acquiring a second sample. The retract command required more torque than the motor could deliver. The clutch then slipped resulting in a "no-go" command that automatically shut down the operation until further commands were received from Earth. The cameras were again used to obtain information about extension of the boom. Knowing the position of the boom made it possible to carry out a series of motions that permitted resumption of the sampling operations.

The third no-go, which occurred on lander II, was caused by a collector head rotation detection switch failure. Scientists believe the fine adjustments made for the collector head had slipped during the flight to Mars, causing the problem. Software and time commands allowed scientists to work around the problem.

Summary

With the exceptions noted, both lander I and lander II performed exceptionally well. Out of 6000 commands only 7 resulted in a "no-go." Four were because of problems encountered while scientists were getting accustomed to operating their instruments in space. When prelaunch sterilization of the spacecraft is considered, along with being rocketed into space and traveling more than 400 million miles to a landing on a planet with a hostile environment, the performance of the landers and their experiments can be termed remarkable.

Orbiter Performance

The Viking orbiter had five basic mission roles: guide the spacecraft to Mars orbit; survey landing sites; support the lander with power, ground generated commands, and down link data during the journey to Mars; carry out scientific studies of Mars from orbit; and act as a communications relay station for the lander.

Infrared Thermal Mapper

The infrared thermal mapper (IRTM) is a multichannel infrared and visual radiometer operating in one visual and five thermal bands. It is capable of making 28 simultaneous measurements in these bands every 1.12 seconds when the instrument is collecting data. The bands were chosen to provide good temperature resolution over the range of surface temperatures expected of from -189°F to 99°F, accurately measure the amount of sunlight reflected from the surface, and determine the atmospheric temperature at an altitude of approximately 15 miles. The instruments were turned on shortly after launch in 1975 for checkout and have been collecting data nearly every day since Mars orbit insertion continuing through 1978.

The multispectral multichannel design and long period of operation has made this the most productive infrared investigation of the planets yet undertaken. Roughly 100 million independent measurements of Mars have been returned from the IRTM. Temperatures measured have ranged from a high of 99°F in southern summer to -234°F in the polar winter. In designing the instrument special attention was devoted to providing each detector with a well defined field of view. This quantity is directly related to the spatial resolution achievable. Measurements at Mars have shown that the field of view is circular with a diameter of 0.3°. At an altitude of 185 miles above the Martian surface, this field of view corresponds to a resolution of 1 mile. This is a significant improvement over previous infrared instruments.

The two instruments have operated as designed with one exception. In October, 1976, the internal mirror on the IRTM carried by Viking orbiter II sometimes failed to stop at one of its commanded positions. This problem was overcome by using the spacecraft computer to direct mirror motion sequences, an approach which effectively eliminated the problem.

Viking Imagining System

From the onset of their activity in June, 1976, the Viking orbiter cameras have performed well. Considering only the physical feat of taking a picture in digital form across 300,000,000 miles of space to Earth where the numbers are translated into images, the accomplishments of Viking are remarkable. Each picture is composed of 1,272,424 picture elements or pixels and each pixel is accorded a grey-scale rating of any of 256 intensities. Furthermore, the number and quality of these images are equally impressive.

The four Viking cameras have taken some 33,766 pictures from June, 1976, to March, 1978, as this is being written. The main types of observations by the orbiter cameras have been: high altitude resolution below 1250 miles, medium at altitudes of up to 6200 miles and low resolution mapping above 6200 miles; three-color imagining and planetary monitoring; and several observational sequences of Mars' two moons, Phobos and Deimos, at ranges of about 2000 miles to less than 60 miles.

The main objectives in this mission were to assist in site certification by finding a safe place for the two Viking landers to land and to improve on the mapping coverage of Mariner 9. Accomplishment of the first task was verified by the safe landing of both landers, the first ever on another planet. The mapping coverage has vastly improved on the low resolution images of Mariner 9. Where Mariner mapped the entire planet at an equivalent of Viking's 14,300 mile coverage, Viking has mapped nearly 50 percent of the planet at medium resolution, and about 1 percent at high resolution. This high resolution coverage was accomplished by a gradual lowering of periapsis or nearest approach of the orbiter to Mars from 930 miles at the beginning of the mission to 185 miles by mid-1977.

In addition to the mapping coverage, the orbiter cameras have made a number of observations more specialized in nature. Observations coordinated with Earth-based observers provided new knowledge of planetary dust storms, of which there were two major ones in 1977 from Feb. 14 to April 29 and from July 7 to August 22. The shadow of Phobos was photographed as it crossed the planet, more accurately locating the lander to within about 1950 feet, and enabling a more refined calculation of the moons' spatial location. Many stereo photographs have also been taken enabling us to better interpret the many new and puzzling geologic features we have found there.

As the Viking cameras bring more of Mars' intriguing surface into sharper focus, the scientists realize how much there is to learn about the complex geologic history of this planet which is only two-thirds the size of Earth, and also how much there is to learn from the vast amount of data we have already acquired.

Orbiter Data Systems

The orbiter on-board data handling was accomplished by three data subsystems: the computer command subsystem, the flight data subsystem, and the data storage subsystem.

Throughout the prime and extended missions, there were no permanent failures to any of the Viking orbiter data subsystems. Several short termed anomalies did occur, but were closed out to be one time failures which could not be repeated under like conditions.

Communications

Several elements provided the required Viking Orbiter (VO) radio communications links with Earth and Mars. The S-band radio assembly provided the Earth to orbiter command link and the orbiter to Earth data transmission link via the S/X-band antenna subsystem. The modulation demodulation subsystem demodulated the Earth to orbiter uplink command signals and generated composite telemetry signals for the modulation of the orbiter to Earth downlink. The relay telemetry and radio subsystem received signals sent to the orbiter from the lander from separation through surface operations of the lander.

The X-band transmitter has power supply and frequency inputs supplied by the S-band radio and feeds signals to the X-band high-gain antenna and thence to Earth.

The operation of all the orbiter communications throughout the period from launch through the Viking extended mission was virtually trouble free. In this time the S-band radio continuously operated for over 20,000 hours, processing spacecraft commands and transmitting back to Earth all the science and engineering data. The orbiter relay equipment made possible the daily links with each of the landers. Operationally the X-band transmitter provided a stable signal to Earth for use by the radio science team and it was also an extremely useful orbiter navigational aid for spacecraft orientation confirmation.

Oblique view of the Argyre impact crater basin highlighted by frost during the Southern hemisphere winter was taken by Viking I, September 8, 1976. Note the high clouds on the limb or horizon.

In the radio assembly the most significant unexpected in-flight event was the uplink AGC anomaly. Non real-time analysis brought to light an offset of -1.7dB in the uplink AGC during one of the many non-propulsive maneuvers. After a great amount of data research, a special in-flight test and comparison of telemetry channels AGC-Course and AGC-Fine, it was concluded that the offset was indeed within the orbiter I S-band receiver. The exact location was not easily determined from telemetry data. The consensus was that the shift was caused by a sudden change in gain within the early stages of the 47 MHz or 9.5 MHz IF amplifiers in the receiver. A continuous record of this shift was maintained in order to catch any failure trend. No further change was ever observed.

The other unexpected changes to radio communications equipment occurred in the S-band receiver VCO rest frequencies. After some six months of flight it became evident that the VCO rest frequencies for both orbiter I and orbiter II had changed from that frequency predicted from pre-launch data. The reason for the offset of rest frequencies was not realized earlier because of the relatively small changes and slow rate of change and very little opportunity for rest frequency observation during two-way operation with doppler effects included. These changes were most likely caused by aging effects in the environment of deep space. The frequencies have stabilized and have not shown any further changes.

Orbiter Temperature Control Subsystem

The temperature control subsystem maintained all temperatures well within their desired range throughout the mission. Because of the cooling required on the launch pad for the radioisotope thermoelectric generators aboard the lander, the propulsion module was cooler than desired for any motor burns. The warm up process was facilitated by admitting solar energy onto the tanks through the solar energy controllers.

Both spacecraft have very similar temperatures at their respective sensors. Orbiter II experienced very long term solar occultations at Mars. Temperatures were maintained within the short term non-operational limits despite the lower power dissipation.

The higher temperatures experienced during propulsion operation for the mid-course corrections, the Mars orbit insertion, and the orbital trims were close to predictions, and were within the allowable temperature limits.

Orbiter Propulsion System

During the Viking primary and extended mission period, eighteen propulsive maneuvers were conducted on orbiter I and fifteen on orbiter II. Maneuver durations ranged from a 1.1-second Mars orbit trim on orbiter I to the 39.4-minute orbit insertion maneuver on orbiter II, the longest duration engine firing in space to date. Propulsive capability remaining at the end of the extended mission is 100 meters-per-second for orbiter I and 42 meters-per-second for orbiter II. No additional maneuvers are currently scheduled.

The pressurant gas remaining in the propulsion helium tank of approximately 2.9 lbs in each orbiter was transferred to the attitude control system by actuation of the pyrotechnic valves in the gas share system on January 7, 1978 for orbiter I and January 15, 1978 for orbiter II. The 2.9 lbs of helium will provide approximately three months additional gas supply to the attitude control system.

Orbiter Pyrotechnic System

The pyrotechnic subsystem on both orbiter I and orbiter II performed flawlessly throughout the primary and extended mission. Of the 22 pyrotechnic devices per orbiter, 18 have been actuated. The four remaining pyrotechnic devices not actuated on either orbiter consist of the final pressurant system isolation valve, the remaining half system gas share valve and the propellant bypass valves. No additional pyrotechnic functions are anticipated for either orbiter.

Viking Science Results Summary

ORBITER IMAGING

Erosional History

Widely varied surface topography revealed equally varied regional environments and erosional processes.

Certain existence of ancient flood plains or channels appeared extremely old, possibly produced billions of years ago by melting of subsurface ice by geothermal heating.

Polygonally pattern terrain girdles on Mars between 45° and 55° could be the result of cooling and shrinking of large regional lava mantles.

Primary erosion process appears to be wind.

Some areas show ancient surface to be softened and subdued, perhaps covered by dust settling from the atmosphere.

Laminating and sculpturing of the north pole is better defined.

Climate

Past climate is active and variable.

Current estimate is stable, long lasting ice age with nearly all of Mar's water frozen into permanent ice caps or within the crust.

Ice at north pole revealed to be dirty, colored by a high content of dust settled from the atmosphere as each layer of water-ice is formed.

Ice canyons at poles formed by different rates of erosion between light and dark layers.

Clouds on Mars are common and diverse, many containing water. Often associated with Tharsis volcanoes.

Large fields of very thin clouds observed in both hemispheres, probably varying combinations of water, dust and carbon dioxide.

Patchy brightness often seen in morning in low areas is probably fog or surface frost.

Dust billows from large, low basins during time of perihelion probably contribute to global atmospheric opacity. Largest dust storms are in southern hemisphere.

Mars Moons

Photos and Deimos were photographed at extremely high resolution to reveal objects as small as 10 feet.

Both moons are cratered to point of saturation.

The moons are colorless, indicating they might be captured asteriods.

Some cratering in secondary chains is probably due to orbital encounters with secondary debris.

GAS CHROMATOGRAPH MASS SPECTROMETER

Atmospheric

Atmospheric composition at the surface agrees with upper atmosphere investigation.

Discovery of 2.5% nitrogen is a most important accomplishment bearing directly on Mars' chemical history and the atmosphere's evolution.

Ratio of argon 36 to argon 40 is 10% of terrestrial value. Abundance of argon 36 is only 1% that of Earth.

Abundances of carbon, oxygen and nitrogen isotopes were measured.

Mars has not outgassed as much as Earth, but present Mars atmosphere is only a small fraction of past atmosphere.

Ancient atmosphere was at least 50 millibars and possibly as much as 500 millibars (Earth's sea level pressure is 1013 millibars).

If Martian atmosphere has not outgassed, it must be contained in the crust and polar caps.

Krypton and xenon discovered in atmosphere, but abundances and values were unobtainable.

Organic

Organic analysis showed surprisingly negative results even though instrument performance and sensitivity was excellent.

Results indicate there is no efficient contemporary process for producing organic compounds on the surface of Mars.

Inasmuch as organic compounds are frequently produced in the universe, having been found in chemistry inventories of meteorites on Earth and in Lunar samples, experiment indicates that the organically sterile samples on Mars have been affected by additional mechanisms.

Additional mechanisms could be destruction of organics by ultraviolet radiation or some exotic chemical oxidation or a combination of both.

It is possible that organic compounds absent on surface are abundant at some depth in crust.

SEISMOMETER

No strong, distant quakes recorded, indicating Mars much less seismically active than Earth.

One regional seismic event with a magnitude of 2.8 was detected by lander II at 68.4 miles from the lander.

Wave reflections from this event indicate crustal thickness of 9 miles and were dampened within minutes indicating possible trapped water and atmosphere in Mars' crust.

RADIO SCIENCE

Radio waves indicated interplanetary medium is affected by solar flares.

Radio data confirmed Einstein's general relativity theory to 5% accuracy in time delay test.

Lander locations determined to within 6 miles.

Mars' radii at landing sites confirmed to accuracy of 328 feet.

Mars' spin rate determined to an accuracy of 2 milliseconds.

Measured density of Mars moons supports theory that they are captured asteroids.

INFRARED THERMAL MAPPER

Global temperatures during primary mission ranged from -225 to 62°F.

Thermal data from north pole cap during summer produced temperatures indicative of water-ice rather than frozen carbon dioxide.

South pole colder than north pole. Although not certain, the south pole cap may be residual dry ice rather than water-ice, making it an entirely different kind of cap than the north pole.

LANDER IMAGING

Lander I - Chryse Planitia

Great range of volcanic rock types and sizes found.

Many dust drifts and windtails on lee-side of rocks observed. Large drift is multilayered indicating deposition and erosion periods.

Fine soil has considerable cohesion quality.

Possible crater profile seen on horizon.

Terrain appears to have been formed by chemical and mechanical destruction of an upper layer of volcanic crust.

Fine material was deposited by winds that faceted some of the rocks.

Ground fog forms late at night and dissipates in late morning.

Lander II - Utopia Planitia

Boulder-strewn, yellowish-brown desert found at landing site.

A plateau seen to the east is a tongue of ejecta from a large nearby impact crater named Mie.

Fine soil similar to Chryse is very fine grained and commonly crusted, otherwise site is similar to lander I.

Late-mission photos show ground frost in early morning.

MAGNETIC PROPERTIES

Magnetic properties of Martian soil are strong, ranging from 1 to 7%. Some of the magnetic material is airborne.

Presence of magnetite indicates Martian soil is not fully weathered or oxidized.

Organic chemistry results support the conclusion that Martian soil composition includes maghemite, which is the principal contributor to the soil's magnetic properties.

METEOROLOGY

Daily temperatures spread by as much as 100°F during the summer but only 9°F during winter.

Both landers recorded similar temperatures and temperature ranges.

Summer temperatures ranged from -25 to -130°F.

Winds are generally mild and their velocities and patterns are remarkably repetitious.

Winds range from 10 mph as an average at both lander sites to gusts of 40 mph. Little change in wind velocities was noted during winter.

Repetitious wind patterns at both sites are believed generated by global circulation and modified by local terrain.

Seasonal atmospheric pressure variations are dramatic, as much as 30% variation. Lowest pressure recorded was 7 millibars with a maximum of 11 millibars.

X-RAY FLUORESCENCE SPECTROMETER

The landing sites lack large variety of rock types common on Earth.

Analysis at both sites shows them to be remarkably similar.

Surface material is composed of iron-rich silicates, iron oxides, and less abundant sulfur and chlorine compounds.

The complex mixture is indicative of a weathering product of chemically basic igneous rock with wide surface exposure.

Best Earth comparison to Mars soil is iron-rich clay, but the general composition is unlike any directly analyzed Earth, Lunar or meteorite samples.

Abundant water had to be present in the past to form the clay weathering products and precipitable salt. The clay that is present could be an important sponge for the water, which is in low abundance in the Mars' atmosphere.

ENTRY/DESCENT

Atmosphere is predominantly carbon dioxide and the composition is well mixed. Carbon dioxide is 95% with small amounts of nitrogen, argon, oxygen, carbon monoxide and nitric oxide.

Composition of the upper atmosphere indicative of a greater density in the past.

Temperature profiles during summer were above the condensation boundary for carbon dioxide, which indicates that fog or haze seen in the northern hemisphere during summer must be composed of condensed water vapor.

MARS ATMOSPHERIC WATER DETECTOR

Water vapor gradually redistributes over the planet during the year.

Maximum abundances were measured during summer at the northern polar cap.

Summer water vapor in the southern polar region was not excessive as expected.

Water vapor abundances decreased sharply with the onset of both major dust storms. Water could be absorbed into the dust, and removed from the atmosphere as the dust settles.

Viking Project Management

Overall management of the Viking project was the responsibility of the Office of Space Science, National Aeronautics and Space Administration (NASA), Washington, D.C. The major portion of the management task was delegated to the Viking project office at NASA's Langley Research Center, Hampton, Virginia.

The Viking project office was assigned six major areas of responsibility as follows:

1) Lander system — Martin Marietta Aerospace, responsible for designing, building and testing the lander;

2. Orbiter system — The Jet Propulsion Laboratory, responsible for designing, building and testing the orbiter;

3) Launch vehicle — The Titan IIIE/Centaur launch vehicle program managed by NASA's Lewis Research Center. The Titan IIIE was provided by the U.S. Air Force Space and Missile Systems Organization (SAMSO) who obtained it from the manufacturer, Martin Marietta Aerospace. The Centaur upper stage was provided by the manufacturer, General Dynamics, Conviar Division;

4) Launch and flight operations — The Kennedy Space Center, Florida;

5) Tracking and data systems — The Jet Propulsion Laboratory, responsible for spacecraft tracking and the return of data via the Deep-Space Network;

6) Mission control and computer center — The Jet Propulsion Laboratory, responsible for the mission control center that controls the spacecraft and the computer center that supports the mission.

The planning and development of scientific investigations, assistance in the development of lander instruments to carry out the investigations and the analysis of scientific data from the mission was the responsibility of 13 science teams consisting of 69 scientists.

The science teams functioned under the direction of a Science Steering Group composed of:

Gerald A. Soffen (Chairman)
Viking Project Office
Langley Research Center

R.S. Young (Vice Chairman)
Viking Program Office
National Aeronautics and Space
  Administration

A. Thomas Young (Secretary)
Viking Project Office
Langley Research Center

The leaders of each of the science teams were also members of the Science Steering Group. The members of the science teams and their leaders are included in the discussions of the results from the Viking project.

The National Aeronautics and Space Administration, the Langley Research Center, the Jet Propulsion Laboratory and Martin Marietta Aerospace were supported by hundreds of contractors and numerous government agencies throughout the United States. Small businesses, minority businesses and businesses in economically depressed areas were encouraged to participate in the Viking project.

The major contractors and other government agencies that participated in Viking are discussed.

NASA RESEARCH CENTERS

Langley Research Center
Hampton, Virginia

The Langley Research Center exercised direct responsibility for NASA to manage the overall day-to-day operations of the Viking project.

The Langley Research Center at Hampton, Virginia, has been in operation since 1917, the first national laboratory for basic research in the science of aeronautics. For 41 years Langley was a laboratory of the former National Advisory Committee for Aeronautics. Since 1958 it has been one of the major aeronautical and space research centers of the National Aeronautics and Space Administration. The mission of the Langley Research Center is to engage in basic and applied research to advance aeronautical and space flight.

The Langley facilities and equipment include a wide array of wind tunnels for investigating design and development problems of aircraft and spacecraft; environmental test structures for preflight determination of the reaction of flight systems and materials; flight simulators, such as those used to study lunar landing, walking on the moon, aircraft maneuvering problems and landing characteristics of space vehicles; specialized laboratories for developing and evaluating advanced life support systems for space flights of extended duration; and analytical computer capabilities.

Ames Research Center
Moffett Field, California

The NASA Ames Research Center (ARC) is the agency's center for planetary biology studies. Under the direction of Dr. Harold Klein the ARC laboratories have developed the scientific models to determine the feasibility of life existing under various conditions throughout the universe.

Much of the fundamental research leading to development of the Viking biology unit was carried out at Ames Research Center.

Lewis Research Center
Cleveland, Ohio

The Lewis Research Center has the overall responsibility for design, development and management of the Centaur program.

MAJOR PROGRAM PARTICIPANTS

Martin Marietta Aerospace
Denver, Colorado

Martin Marietta Aerospace, at its space center near Denver, Colorado, was responsible to NASA's Langley Research Center for overall integration of the Viking project and was prime contractor for the Viking lander and its systems. This included designing, testing and building the lander and managing all lander subcontracts. Also included was the design and support of the launch and flight operations systems.

Martin Marietta also designed and built the photosensor array for the Viking cameras, the temperature transducers that measured Mars' atmospheric temperatures, and the X-ray fluorescence spectrometer, which detected the various chemicals in the Martian soil.

Martin Marietta also built the two Titan IIIE launch vehicles for the two Viking spacecraft.

Jet Propulsion Laboratory
Pasadena, California

The Jet Propulsion Laboratory (JPL) was primarily responsible for the Viking orbiter and the mission control center. JPL built for NASA the highly successful series of Mariner spacecraft that have flown by and orbited Mars during the last decade to provide the information that made the Viking project possible.

The Space Flight Operations Facility at JPL is the location of the Viking mission control center. Engineers and scientists there communicated with Viking, sending commands for the spacecraft's operation and receiving data for scientific analysis.

JPL also controls the Deep-Space Network.

Space and Missile Systems Organization
Los Angeles, California

SAMSO is the U.S. government agency responsible for developing the Titan III launch vehicle. The latest version of this launch vehicle is the Titan IIIE/Centaur developed by NASA to launch planetary probes requiring high-energy launches.

The SAMSO 6555 Aerospace Test Wing at Cape Canaveral Air Force Station manages the Titan launch facility and supports NASA in the conduct of launch operations for the Titan III/Centaur.

Litton Industries
Woodland Hills, California

The Litton Industries Guidance and Control Systems Division at its facility located in Woodland Hills, California, was responsible for production and integration of the design technology to be used in the gas chromatograph mass spectrometer for the NASA Langley Viking Mars probe.

The division tested and produced the GCMS device that investigated the makeup of the Martian atmosphere and provided for the organic molecular analysis of components in the Martian soil.

Litton Industries has been active in computer-augmented aerospace ground support equipment for the past 10 years and has participated in other NASA projects, particularly in the devleopment of the data automatic subsystems for the Mariner program.

MARTIN MARIETTA SUBCONTRACTORS

Teledyne Ryan Aeronautical
San Diego, California

Teledyne Ryan Aeronautical, Electronic and Space Systems, in San Diego, California, was the subcontractor for the radar altimeter and the terminal descent and landing radar used on the Viking lander. This included designing, testing and building both radars plus designing, building and testing special test equipment for checkout of the radars.

Sheldahl, Inc.
Northfield, Minnesota

Sheldahl, Inc. designed and built four 35 million cubic foot heavy-load-carrying, high-altitude balloons used for the BLDT (Balloon Launched Decelerator Test) program for the Viking lander. These balloons performed their function with 100 percent success. Sheldahl also designed the patented disk-gap-band parachute used as part of that deceleration system.

Sheldahl developed the materials and processes and completed the fabrication of the two flight, one backup, and four test bioshields used to encapsulate the Viking lander.

Sheldahl also fabricated the lander leg covers used to contain the frangible shock absorbing material so it didn't contaminate Mars' surface when crushed on landing.

RCA Astro-Electronics Division
Princeton, New Jersey

RCA Astro-Electronics Division, also known as the RCA Space Center, is located near Princeton, New Jersey. The division, as a subcontractor to Martin Marietta Aerospace, was responsible for the Viking lander communications subsystem.

RCA designed, built and tested the lander subsystem, which consisted of an ultrahigh frequency (UHF) radio transmitter and antenna for beaming information to the orbiter, an S-band high-gain antenna for broadcasting directly to Earth, and an S-band low-gain unit to receive commands direct from Earth.

RCA supplied three communication systems for the Viking lander.

TRW Inc.
Redondo Beach, California

TRW built the biology and meteorology instruments on the Viking lander. The instruments were built and tested at the TRW Systems Group space park in Redondo Beach, California.

TRW Systems is a major supplier of satellites and spacecraft to the Department of Defense, NASA and commercial users. They also provide software and system engineering services for major military programs.

Celesco Industries
Costa Mesa, California

Celesco Industries built the surface sampler arm, housing and drive mechanism that picked up the Mars surface samples and delivered them to the lander instruments.

United Technologies Corporation
Hamilton Standard Division
Windsor Locks, Connecticut

Hamilton Standard was responsible for designing and building the inertial reference units for the Viking landers.

The corporation's experience in guidance and navigation equipment includes the inertial guidance sensor assemblies for the Apollo lunar module spacecraft and the guidance sensor package for NASA's Delta launch vehicles.

Itek Corporation
Optical Systems Division
Lexington, Massachusetts

Itek Corporation was responsible to Martin Marietta Aerospace for all aspects of the Viking lander camera system used for onsite photography during the Viking mission. Itek produced and tested the cameras and their supporting Earth-based ground reconstruction sets. Throughout the project, Itek worked closely with the team of scientists responsible for the imagery experiment to develop an accurate and reliable instrument.

In addition to the imaging system's hardware, Itek also provided all computer software necessary to operate and control the cameras and to drive the ground reconstruction equipment in reconstructing photos.

Goodyear Aerospace Corporation
Akron, Ohio

Goodyear Aerospace Corporation, at its Akron head-quarters, was responsible to Martin Marietta Aerospace as a major subcontractor for the decelerator system employed on NASA's Viking lander. This included designing, testing and building the decelerator system and managing subtier suppliers and subcontractors.

Honeywell Aerospace Division
St. Petersburg, Florida

Honeywell, under subcontract to Martin Marietta Aerospace, was responsible for designing, manufacturing and testing the Viking lander guidance, control, and sequencing computer and data storage memory.

Honeywell also designed and continues to manufacture the guidance system for the Centaur booster, second stage of the Viking launch vehicle.

Honeywell has been a contractor in every significant NASA space program to date, including all manned space programs from Mercury through Apollo and Skylab, and all the Mariner Mars exploratory series that helped pave the way for Viking.

Bendix Aerospace Systems Division
Ann Arbor, Michigan

Bendix was responsible to Martin Marietta for two of the entry science instruments — the upper atmospheric mass spectrometer and the retarding potential analyzer and one Martian surface instrument, the seismometer. All aspects of the three instruments including design, fabrication, assembly and test were conducted at the Bendix Ann Arbor, Michigan facilities.

Bendix has extensive experience in space instruments that ranges from sounding rocket experiments to the Apollo lunar surface experiment packages, the remote scientific stations which continue to relay science from the moon more than five years after their initial deployment.

Rocket Research Corporation
Redmond, Washington

Rocket Research Corporation, under contract to Martin Marietta Aerospace, was responsible for developing and manufacturing the throttleable monopropellant hydrazine landing engines. In addition to the landing engines, Rocket Research was also responsible for delivery of the 8.7 pound-foot monopropellant hydrazine roll control and deorbit engines.

Rocket Research provides engines and control systems for many NASA spacecraft including the earth resources technology satellite (ERTS and LANDSAT), synchronous meteorological satellite (SMS), application technology satellite (ATS), and the geostationary operational environmental satellite (GOES).